MY LIFE IN GRAPHS

A GUIDED JOURNAL

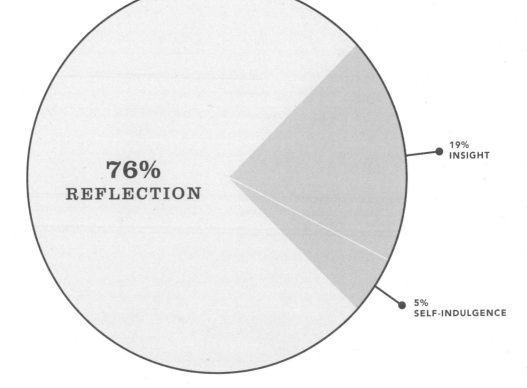

76%
REFLECTION

19%
INSIGHT

5%
SELF-INDULGENCE

KNOCK KNOCK®

VENICE, CALIFORNIA

CREATED AND PUBLISHED BY KNOCK KNOCK
DISTRIBUTED BY WHO'S THERE INC.
VENICE, CA 90291
KNOCKKNOCKSTUFF.COM

ISBN: 978-160106128-7
UPC: 825703-50054-7

COULDN'T WE ALL BENEFIT FROM ASSEMBLING THE SUM OF OUR PARTS IN ORDER TO BETTER UNDERSTAND THE WHOLE?

By analyzing our beliefs, habits, quirks, and unhealthy obsessions, we can establish a pattern and maybe even solve the baffling brainteaser of our identity. Fortunately, navel-gazing is hardwired into us; whether we choose self-help programs, daily therapy sessions, or journaling, we intuitively know that in order to make sense of the world we must first make sense of ourselves. While it may be true that everyone is an island, it's also true that no one was given a map—but the next best thing must surely be a graph.

Life is a series of checks and balances, a numbers game of probabilities and theorems that, no matter what, will throw statistically improbable anomalies your way. And much like the complex equation of life, so too are our personalities littered with vexing variables, confounding calculations, and unknown quantities. Let's face it—like math, the human condition is frustrating, complicated, and liable to provoke a headache.

While there is no set formula for something as abstract as self-reflection, we can look to geometry for cues. Famous French philosopher René Descartes encountered a similar quandary in the heady days of the Scientific Revolution, and developed the coordinate plane as a result. By rendering a fussy numeric principle in graphic terms, Descartes advanced our understanding of how the world functions in incalculably numerous ways. If a graph can represent something as confounding as higher mathematics, then surely it can do the same for something just as impenetrable—namely, us.

Modern-day life is decidedly more complex than it was during the seventeenth century. From websites to phone apps to the evening news, our technocratic culture is increasingly informing our preference toward visual thinking. Thankfully, we now have even more ways to plot, chart, and sketch our very existence—the infographic. Forget talking about your feelings, now you can render them in glorious, eye-catching diagrams.

What's more, graphs are excellent at absorbing large quantities of information and transforming them into one easily digested image. The amount of data we receive every day is literally mind-boggling: in 2008, the *New York Times* reported that information overload was costing the national economy around $650 billion a year as a result of lost productivity. With that much interference it's no surprise that we find it difficult to make sense of something as simple as, say, our eating habits. A graph allows you to plug in the necessary information, such as what you eat for lunch, and then presents a coherent representation of what that data actually means—even if it only confirms that you generally stuff yourself full of french fries.

Of course, different kinds of charts are better suited to particular types of information. Luckily, graphs are infinitely versatile. Line graphs and timelines, for instance, make it easy to plot changes that take place over a span of time (such as the frequency with which we watch television); pie charts and Venn diagrams depict proportionate values with ease and aplomb (the shows that we prefer); and bar graphs do an amazing job of comparison (our obsession with reality shows vs. the evening news). No matter how complicated (or simple) our personalities are, there is sure to be a graph—or many—that will give us a unique perspective on who we really are.

My Life in Graphs includes a variety of diagrams, tables, and charts for plotting almost every aspect of your personality, from relationships to emotional hang-ups to employment to the meaning of life. Don't feel pressured to work straight through the book; instead start by flipping through the pages and tackling the topics that strike you as relevant to your current state of mind. As the pages fill up, remember to take a step back every once in a while and look for larger themes as they develop. You may discover that you're a stress case, have accomplished more than you realized, or simply have an inexplicable attraction to snake handlers. Finally, in *My Life in Graphs*, you will find the elusive formula that poets and philosophers have long thought to be impossible— a linear explanation of the messy problems of human existence.

OVERVIEW OF GRAPH TOPICS

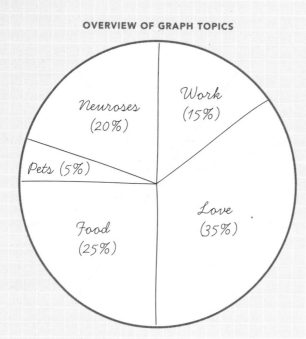

[Pie Charts]

Pie charts indicate the proportionate components and values of the subject matter provided. Apply percentage values to each subject and then outline and label accordingly. Note that each pie slice represents 10 percent while the completed graph should total 100 percent. Suggestions for potential data are provided throughout, although users are encouraged to add their own responses. For comparative or multiple graphs, fill in each graph accordingly.

[Bar Graphs]

Bar graphs provide a comparative analysis of the different elements of the subject matter provided. Indicate the level of each element along the bottom (the x-axis) based upon the scale found on the left side (the y-axis) by outlining a bar to represent the appropriate level. In some instances, users are prompted to fill in the necessary elements along the x-axis and provide suggestions for potential data. For comparative or multiple graphs, fill in each graph accordingly.

COMPARATIVE PREFERENCE FOR GRAPH TYPES

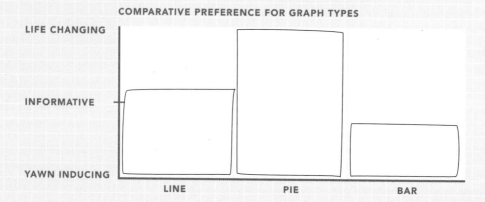

[Line Graphs]

Line graphs indicate the chronological relationship of the subject matter provided. Draw points based upon the years or time periods indicated along the bottom of the graph (the x-axis) and the rate of activity indicated along the scale on the left side (the y-axis). When points are complete, connect the dots in order of sequence with lines. Milestones are provided to help define the appropriate fluctuations, although users are encouraged to provide their own. For comparative or multiple graphs, fill in each graph accordingly.

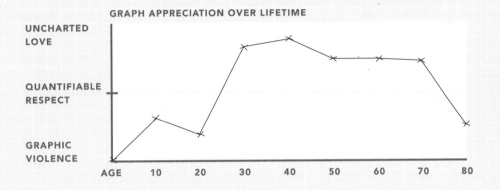

GRAPH APPRECIATION OVER LIFETIME

UNCHARTED
LOVE

QUANTIFIABLE
RESPECT

GRAPHIC
VIOLENCE

AGE   10   20   30   40   50   60   70   80

[Venn Diagrams]

Venn diagrams represent the composite and interactive elements of the subject matter provided. Within each circle, write one of the three elements that you feel best represents the central theme. Suggestions for potential data are provided throughout, although users are encouraged to add their own responses. For multiple diagrams, fill in each accordingly.

ATTRIBUTES OF A SUCCESSFUL GRAPH

Illuminating

INSIGHT

Visually Appealing

Completely Filled In

[Scattergraphs]

Scattergraphs provide an assessment of the relationship of multiple elements to the ideal provided condition at the center of the circle. Label elements on the graph's concentric rings in order, from most to least related to the central theme. Suggestions for potential elements are provided although users are encouraged to add their own.

COMPARATIVE SITUATIONS CONDUCIVE TO GRAPHING

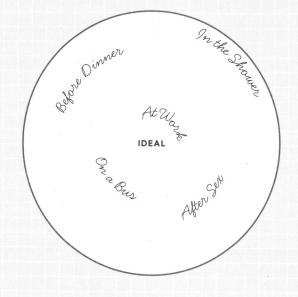

Before Dinner

In the Shower

At Work

IDEAL

On a Bus

After Sex

GRAPHING PROFICIENCY OVER LIFETIME

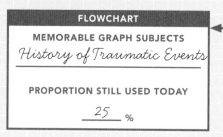

BAR
MEMORABLE GRAPH SUBJECTS
Relative Age Analysis
PROPORTION STILL USED TODAY
95 %

[Flowcharts]

Flowcharts represent a timeline of the defining elements that compose the subject provided. Under each field, fill in the written and numeric prompts based on the corresponding time period indicated.

PIE
MEMORABLE GRAPH SUBJECTS
Primary Thoughts
PROPORTION STILL USED TODAY
73 %

FLOWCHART
MEMORABLE GRAPH SUBJECTS
History of Traumatic Events
PROPORTION STILL USED TODAY
25 %

[Mirror Graphs]

Mirror graphs enable users to compare the relative merits of the subject provided. For each graph, use a < or > symbol to indicate the relative position of each element on the graph's spectrum according to their relationship to both ends. Suggestions for potential elements are provided although users are encouraged to add their own.

ANALYSIS OF GRAPH-MAKING TOOLS

TOOL #1: COMPASS

USEFUL	>	USELESS

TOOL #2: GEOMETRY MANUAL

USEFUL	<	USELESS

ANALYSIS OF GRAPHABLE DATA

INFORMATIVE

Family life

Stress level

Work ethic

Internet usage

Sex life

IMMEASURABLE

OFF THE CHARTS

EMBARRASSING

[Index Graphs]

An index graph consists of four quadrants that each represent a combination of relative strengths and weaknesses (as indicated by the prompts of the graph compass). Write in the provided (or your own) data points within the appropriate quadrant to assess the subject.

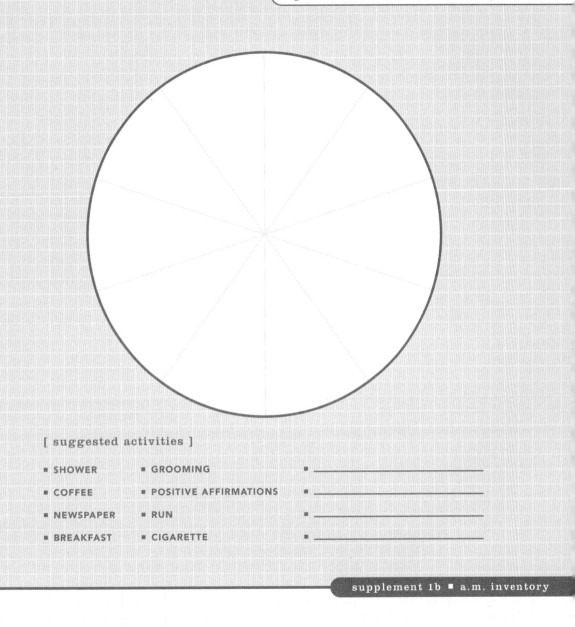

[suggested activities]

- SHOWER
- COFFEE
- NEWSPAPER
- BREAKFAST

- GROOMING
- POSITIVE AFFIRMATIONS
- RUN
- CIGARETTE

- _____
- _____
- _____
- _____

supplement 1b ■ a.m. inventory

- USUAL BEDTIME: _____
- HOURS OF SLEEP PER NIGHT: _____
- SNOOZE BUTTON HIT: _____

- USUAL WAKE-UP TIME: _____
- DURATION OF COMMUTE: _____
- WORK START TIME: _____

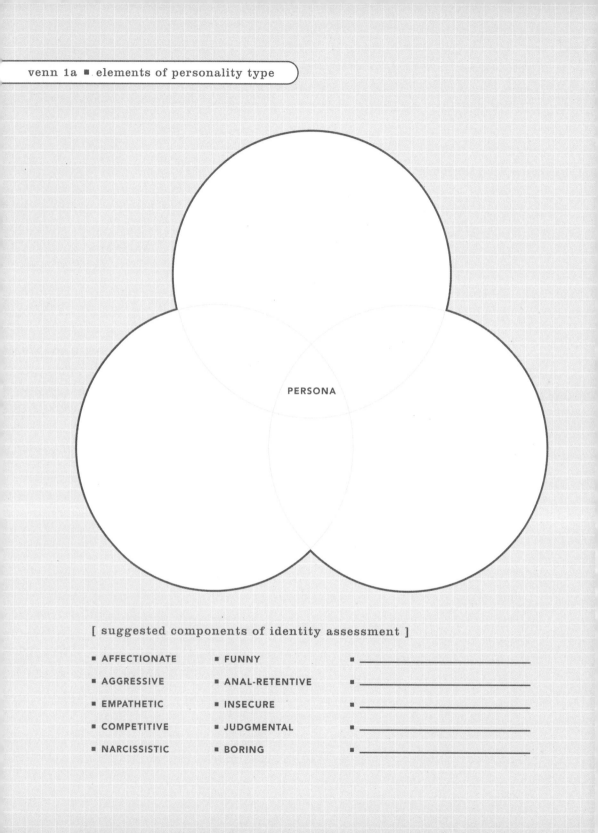

PERSONA

[suggested components of identity assessment]

- AFFECTIONATE
- AGGRESSIVE
- EMPATHETIC
- COMPETITIVE
- NARCISSISTIC

- FUNNY
- ANAL-RETENTIVE
- INSECURE
- JUDGMENTAL
- BORING

- _____
- _____
- _____
- _____
- _____

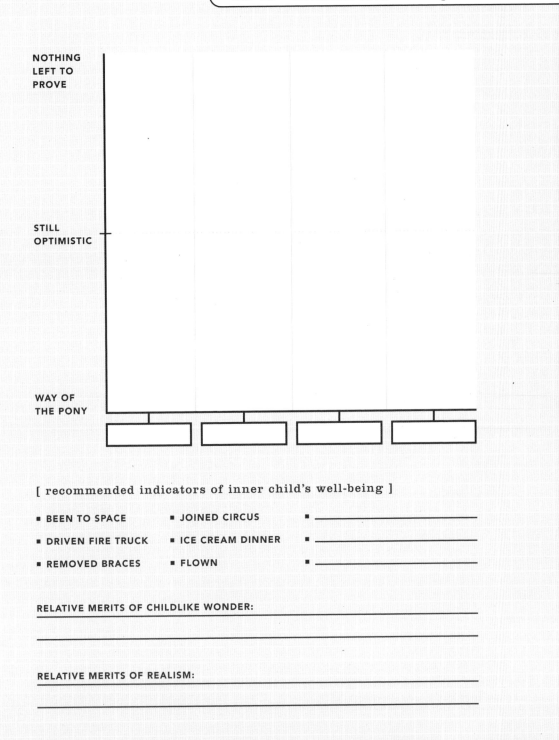

NOTHING
LEFT TO
PROVE

STILL
OPTIMISTIC

WAY OF
THE PONY

[recommended indicators of inner child's well-being]

- BEEN TO SPACE   ■ JOINED CIRCUS   ■ _____
- DRIVEN FIRE TRUCK ■ ICE CREAM DINNER   ■ _____
- REMOVED BRACES   ■ FLOWN   ■ _____

RELATIVE MERITS OF CHILDLIKE WONDER: _____
_____

RELATIVE MERITS OF REALISM: _____
_____

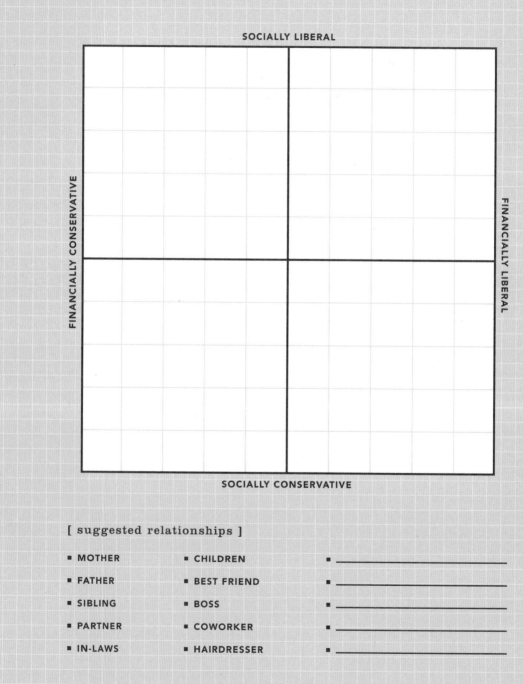

SOCIALLY LIBERAL

FINANCIALLY CONSERVATIVE

FINANCIALLY LIBERAL

SOCIALLY CONSERVATIVE

[suggested relationships]

- MOTHER
- FATHER
- SIBLING
- PARTNER
- IN-LAWS

- CHILDREN
- BEST FRIEND
- BOSS
- COWORKER
- HAIRDRESSER

- _____
- _____
- _____
- _____
- _____

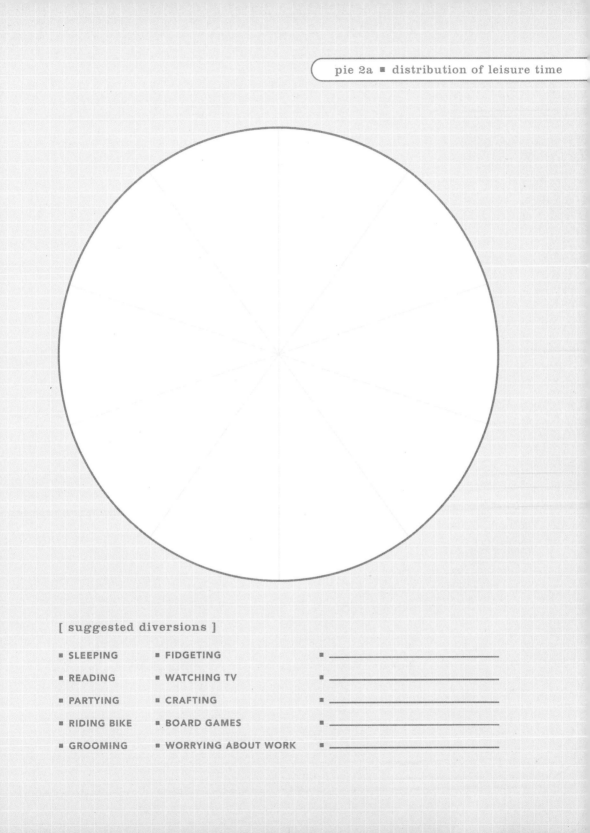

[suggested diversions]

- SLEEPING
- READING
- PARTYING
- RIDING BIKE
- GROOMING

- FIDGETING
- WATCHING TV
- CRAFTING
- BOARD GAMES
- WORRYING ABOUT WORK

- _____
- _____
- _____
- _____
- _____

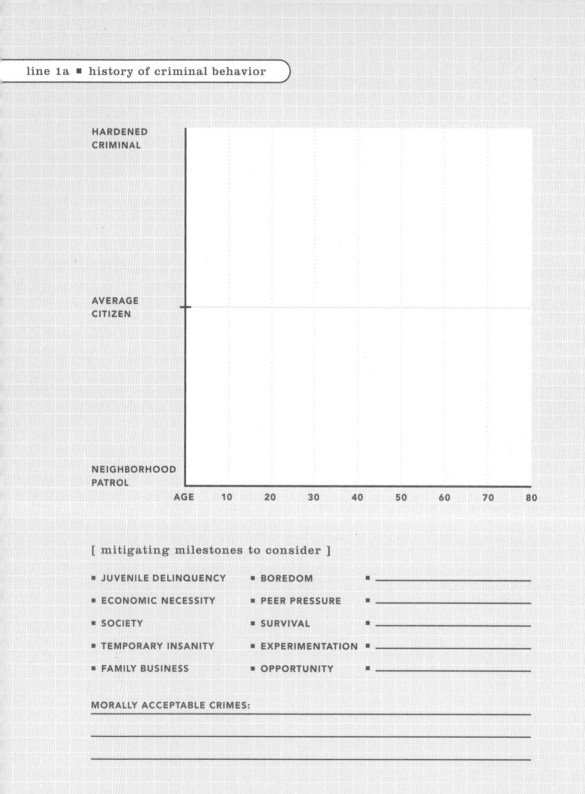

HARDENED
CRIMINAL

AVERAGE
CITIZEN

NEIGHBORHOOD
PATROL

AGE   10   20   30   40   50   60   70   80

[mitigating milestones to consider]

▪ JUVENILE DELINQUENCY   ▪ BOREDOM   ▪ _____

▪ ECONOMIC NECESSITY   ▪ PEER PRESSURE   ▪ _____

▪ SOCIETY   ▪ SURVIVAL   ▪ _____

▪ TEMPORARY INSANITY   ▪ EXPERIMENTATION   ▪ _____

▪ FAMILY BUSINESS   ▪ OPPORTUNITY   ▪ _____

MORALLY ACCEPTABLE CRIMES: _____

_____

_____

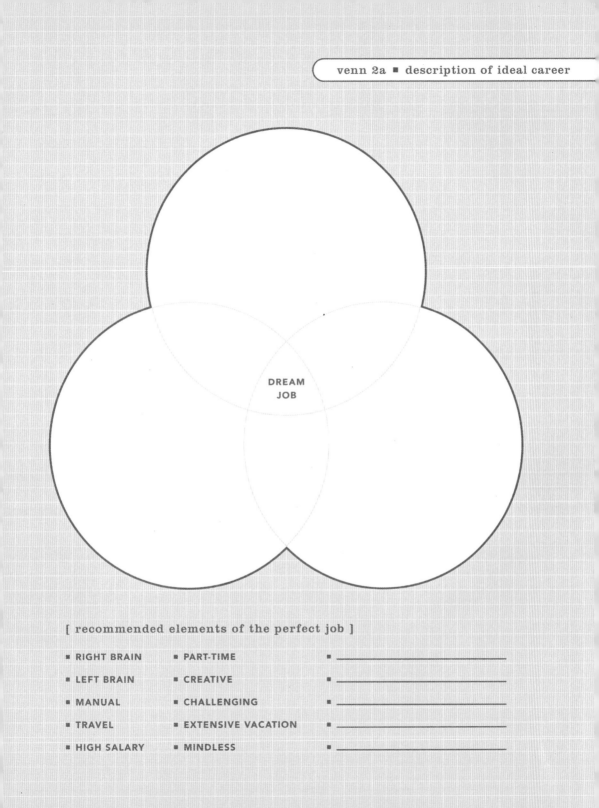

DREAM
JOB

[recommended elements of the perfect job]

- RIGHT BRAIN   - PART-TIME   ▪ _____
- LEFT BRAIN   - CREATIVE   ▪ _____
- MANUAL   - CHALLENGING   ▪ _____
- TRAVEL   - EXTENSIVE VACATION ▪ _____
- HIGH SALARY   - MINDLESS   ▪ _____

TOPIC #1: _____

STUBBORN	OBJECTIVE

TOPIC #2: _____

STUBBORN	OBJECTIVE

TOPIC #3: _____

STUBBORN	OBJECTIVE

TOPIC #4: _____

STUBBORN	OBJECTIVE

TOPIC #5: _____

STUBBORN	OBJECTIVE

[suggested areas of debate]

- POLITICS
- MUSIC
- ART

- FOOD
- OTHER PEOPLE'S FLAWS
- EX-LOVERS

- _____
- _____
- _____

PROS OF TRYING NEW THINGS: _____
_____
_____

CONS OF TRYING NEW THINGS: _____
_____
_____

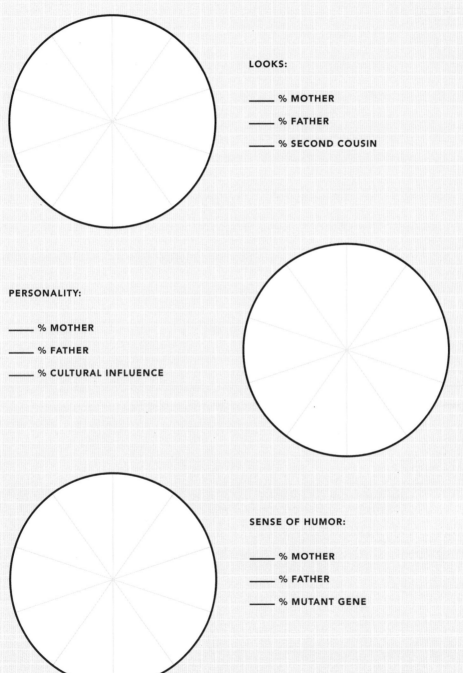

LOOKS:

_____ % MOTHER

_____ % FATHER

_____ % SECOND COUSIN

PERSONALITY:

_____ % MOTHER

_____ % FATHER

_____ % CULTURAL INFLUENCE

SENSE OF HUMOR:

_____ % MOTHER

_____ % FATHER

_____ % MUTANT GENE

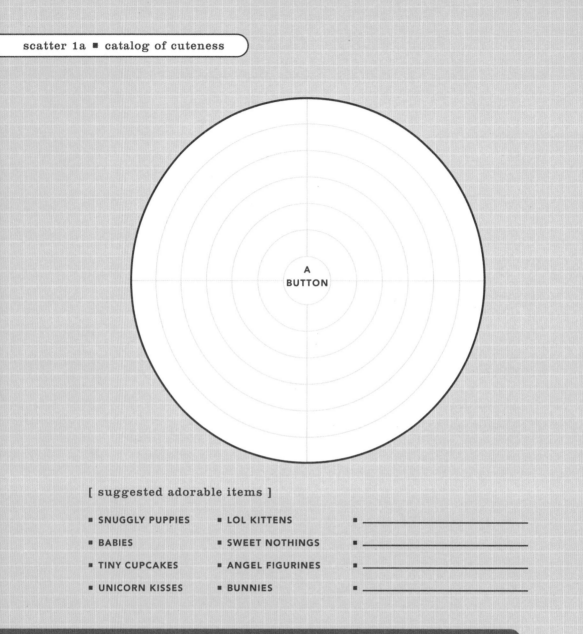

[suggested adorable items]

- SNUGGLY PUPPIES   ■ LOL KITTENS   ■ _____
- BABIES   ■ SWEET NOTHINGS   ■ _____
- TINY CUPCAKES   ■ ANGEL FIGURINES   ■ _____
- UNICORN KISSES   ■ BUNNIES   ■ _____

supplement 1b ■ mathematical breakdown regarding the importance of cute

[>, <, (or) =]

- CUTE _____ INTELLIGENCE   ■ CUTE _____ SEX APPEAL
- CUTE _____ RATIONALITY   ■ CUTE _____ RESPECT
- CUTE _____ INTEGRITY   ■ CUTE _____ KNOWLEDGE OF CURRENT EVENTS

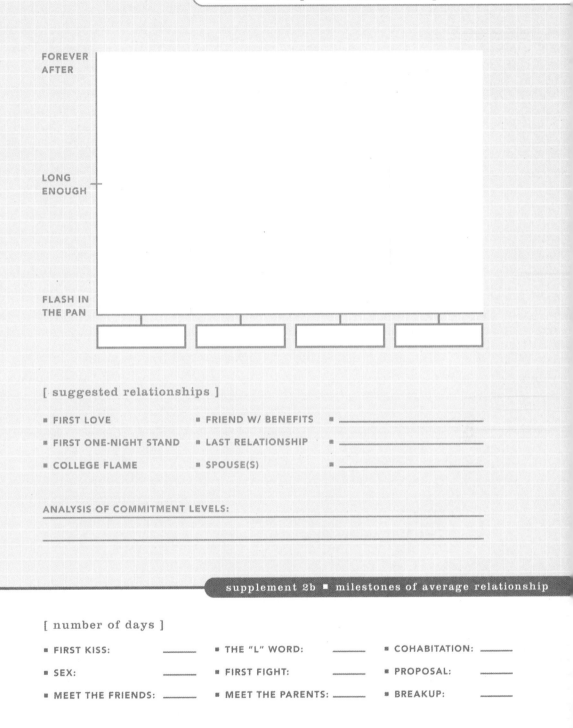

FOREVER
AFTER

LONG
ENOUGH

FLASH IN
THE PAN

[suggested relationships]

■ FIRST LOVE   ■ FRIEND W/ BENEFITS   ■ _____

■ FIRST ONE-NIGHT STAND   ■ LAST RELATIONSHIP   ■ _____

■ COLLEGE FLAME   ■ SPOUSE(S)   ■ _____

ANALYSIS OF COMMITMENT LEVELS: _____

_____

[number of days]

■ FIRST KISS: _____   ■ THE "L" WORD: _____   ■ COHABITATION: _____

■ SEX: _____   ■ FIRST FIGHT: _____   ■ PROPOSAL: _____

■ MEET THE FRIENDS: _____   ■ MEET THE PARENTS: _____   ■ BREAKUP: _____

BEST FRIEND: _____

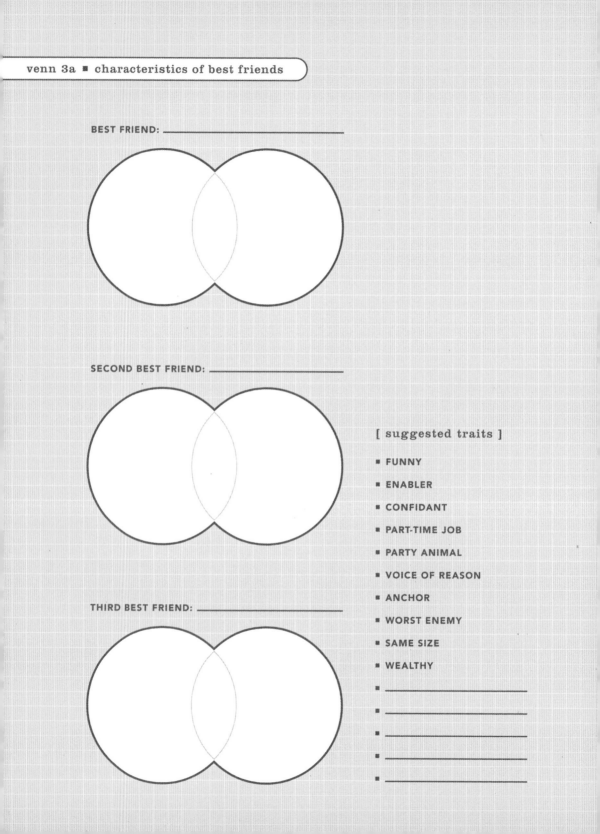

SECOND BEST FRIEND: _____

THIRD BEST FRIEND: _____

[suggested traits]

- FUNNY
- ENABLER
- CONFIDANT
- PART-TIME JOB
- PARTY ANIMAL
- VOICE OF REASON
- ANCHOR
- WORST ENEMY
- SAME SIZE
- WEALTHY
- _____
- _____
- _____
- _____
- _____

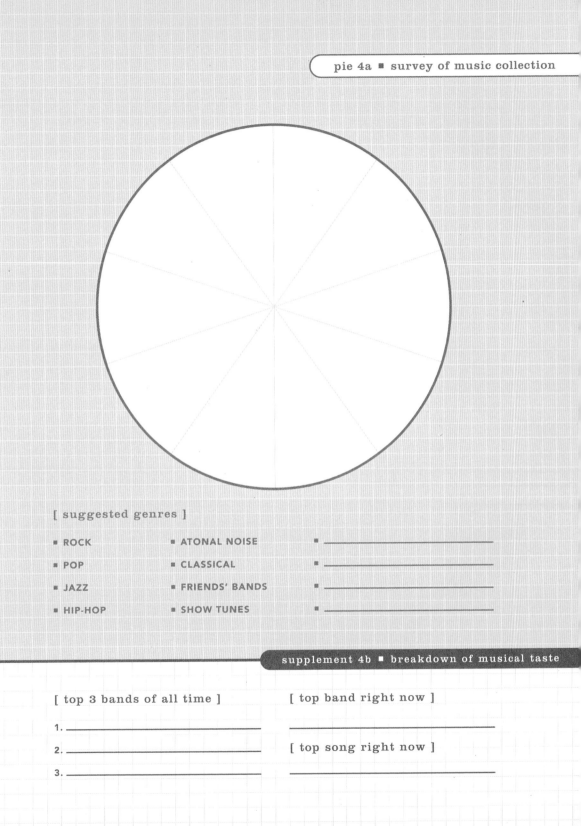

[suggested genres]

- ROCK
- POP
- JAZZ
- HIP-HOP

- ATONAL NOISE
- CLASSICAL
- FRIENDS' BANDS
- SHOW TUNES

- _____
- _____
- _____
- _____

supplement 4b ■ breakdown of musical taste

[top 3 bands of all time]

1. _____

2. _____

3. _____

[top band right now]

_____

[top song right now]

_____

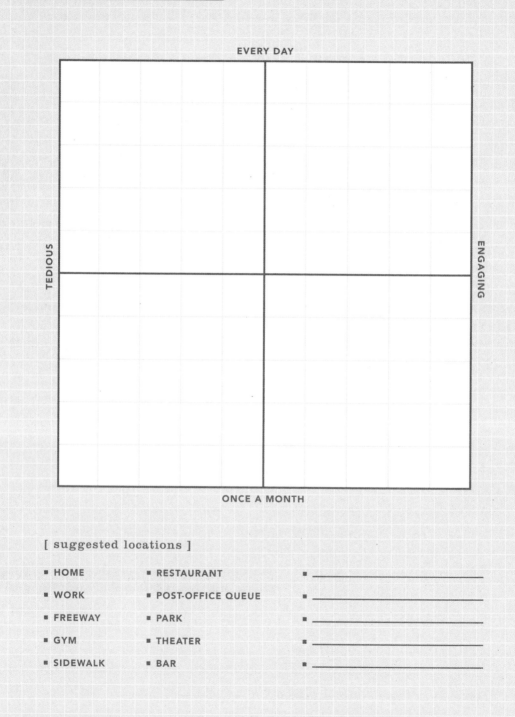

EVERY DAY

TEDIOUS

ENGAGING

ONCE A MONTH

[suggested locations]

■ HOME   ■ RESTAURANT   ■ _____

■ WORK   ■ POST-OFFICE QUEUE   ■ _____

■ FREEWAY   ■ PARK   ■ _____

■ GYM   ■ THEATER   ■ _____

■ SIDEWALK   ■ BAR   ■ _____

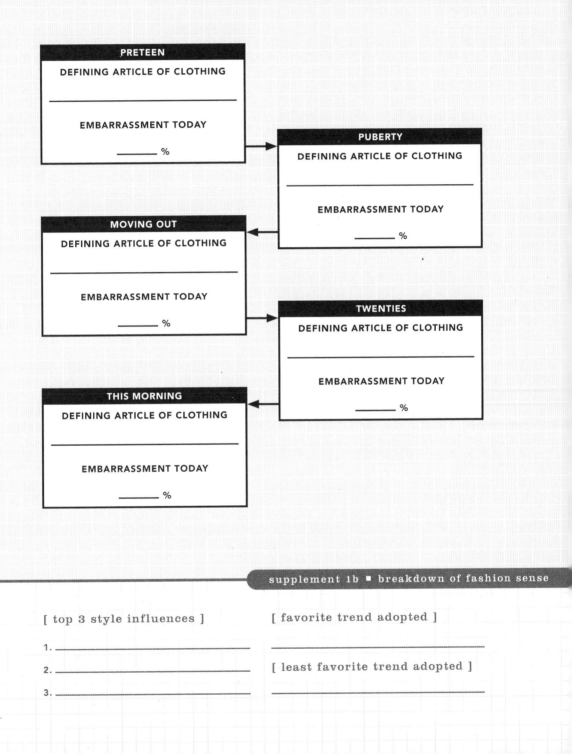

PRETEEN

DEFINING ARTICLE OF CLOTHING

_____

EMBARRASSMENT TODAY

_____ %

PUBERTY

DEFINING ARTICLE OF CLOTHING

_____

EMBARRASSMENT TODAY

_____ %

MOVING OUT

DEFINING ARTICLE OF CLOTHING

_____

EMBARRASSMENT TODAY

_____ %

TWENTIES

DEFINING ARTICLE OF CLOTHING

_____

EMBARRASSMENT TODAY

_____ %

THIS MORNING

DEFINING ARTICLE OF CLOTHING

_____

EMBARRASSMENT TODAY

_____ %

supplement 1b ■ breakdown of fashion sense

[top 3 style influences]

1. _____

2. _____

3. _____

[favorite trend adopted]

_____

[least favorite trend adopted]

_____

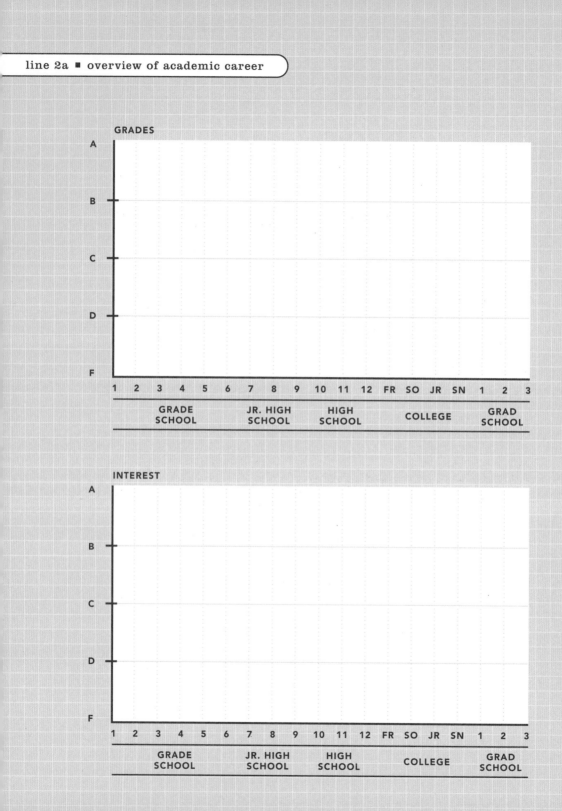

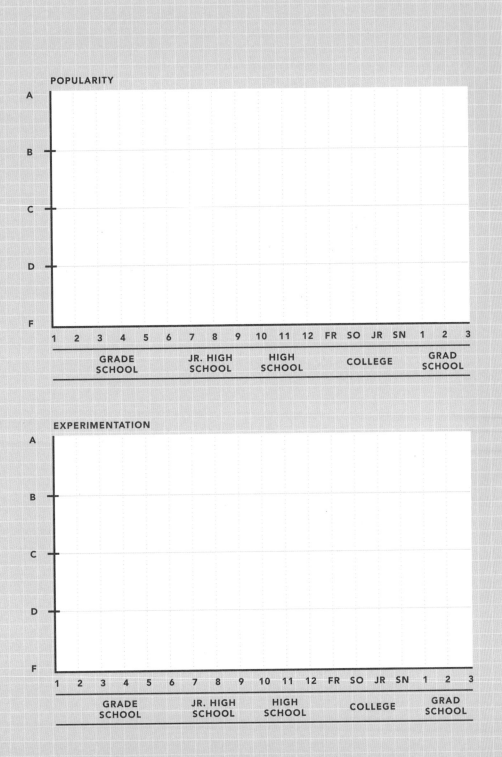

POPULARITY

A
B
C
D
F

1 2 3 4 5 6 7 8 9 10 11 12 FR SO JR SN 1 2 3

GRADE
SCHOOL   JR. HIGH   HIGH   COLLEGE   GRAD
           SCHOOL   SCHOOL   SCHOOL

EXPERIMENTATION

A
B
C
D
F

1 2 3 4 5 6 7 8 9 10 11 12 FR SO JR SN 1 2 3

GRADE
SCHOOL   JR. HIGH   HIGH   COLLEGE   GRAD
           SCHOOL   SCHOOL   SCHOOL

pie 5a ■ primary reasons for relationship quarrels

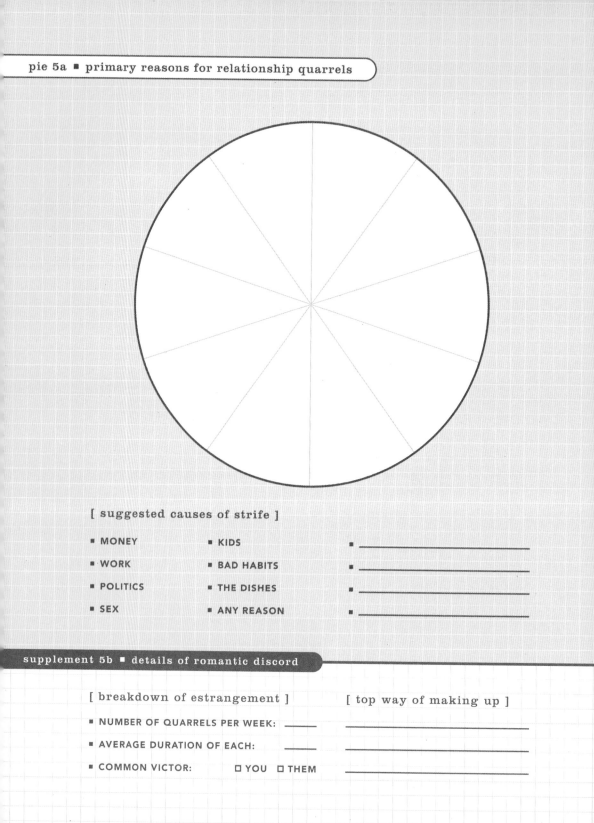

[suggested causes of strife]

- MONEY
- WORK
- POLITICS
- SEX

- KIDS
- BAD HABITS
- THE DISHES
- ANY REASON

- _____
- _____
- _____
- _____

supplement 5b ■ details of romantic discord

[breakdown of estrangement]

- NUMBER OF QUARRELS PER WEEK: _____
- AVERAGE DURATION OF EACH: _____
- COMMON VICTOR: ☐ YOU ☐ THEM

[top way of making up]

_____
_____
_____

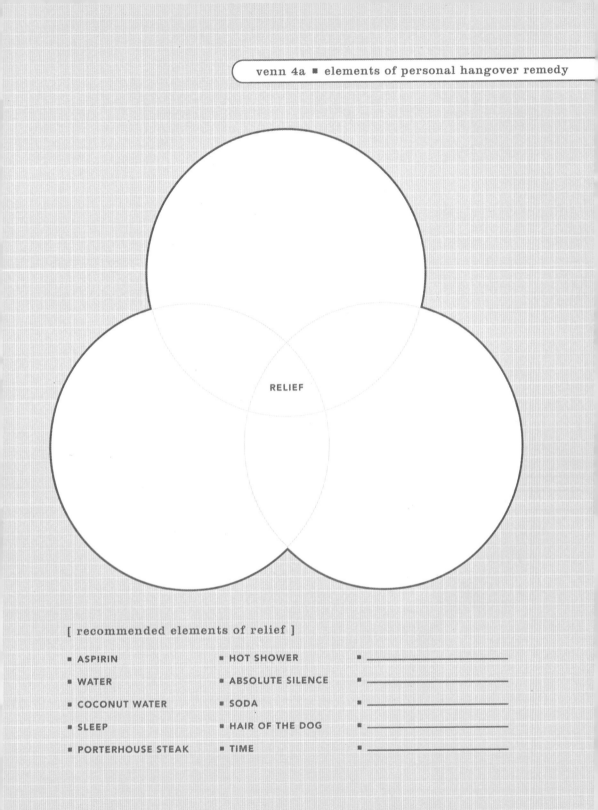

RELIEF

[recommended elements of relief]

- ASPIRIN
- WATER
- COCONUT WATER
- SLEEP
- PORTERHOUSE STEAK

- HOT SHOWER
- ABSOLUTE SILENCE
- SODA
- HAIR OF THE DOG
- TIME

- _____
- _____
- _____
- _____
- _____

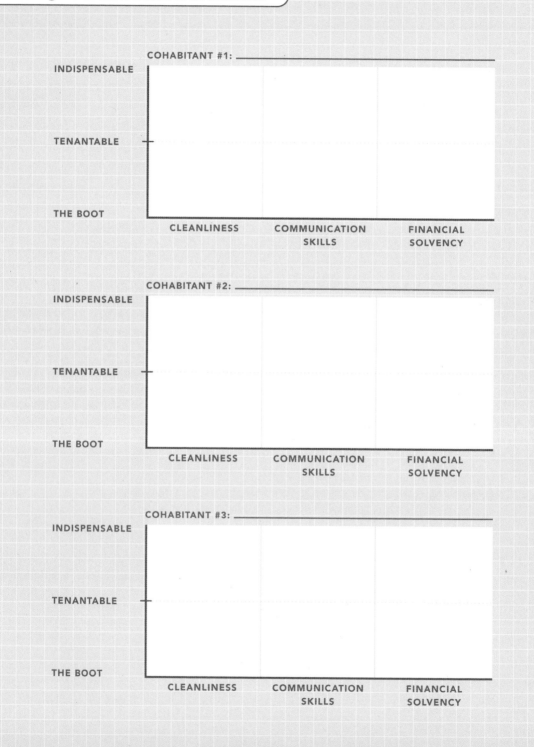

COHABITANT #1: _____

INDISPENSABLE

TENANTABLE

THE BOOT

CLEANLINESS   COMMUNICATION SKILLS   FINANCIAL SOLVENCY

COHABITANT #2: _____

INDISPENSABLE

TENANTABLE

THE BOOT

CLEANLINESS   COMMUNICATION SKILLS   FINANCIAL SOLVENCY

COHABITANT #3: _____

INDISPENSABLE

TENANTABLE

THE BOOT

CLEANLINESS   COMMUNICATION SKILLS   FINANCIAL SOLVENCY

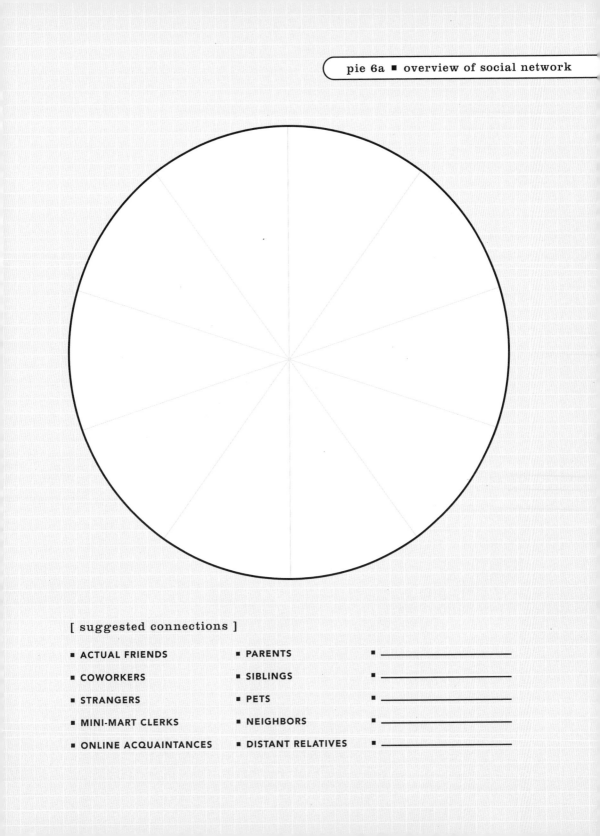

[suggested connections]

- ACTUAL FRIENDS
- COWORKERS
- STRANGERS
- MINI-MART CLERKS
- ONLINE ACQUAINTANCES

- PARENTS
- SIBLINGS
- PETS
- NEIGHBORS
- DISTANT RELATIVES

- _____
- _____
- _____
- _____
- _____

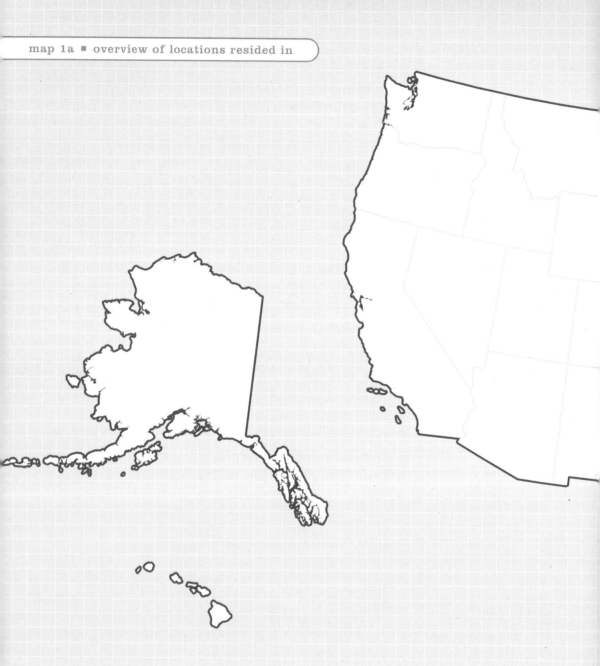

instructions:
[fill in the states where you have lived]

supplement 1b ■ breakdown of preference

[cities you have resided in]   [most habitable]

1. _____   _____

2. _____   [years resided]

3. _____   _____

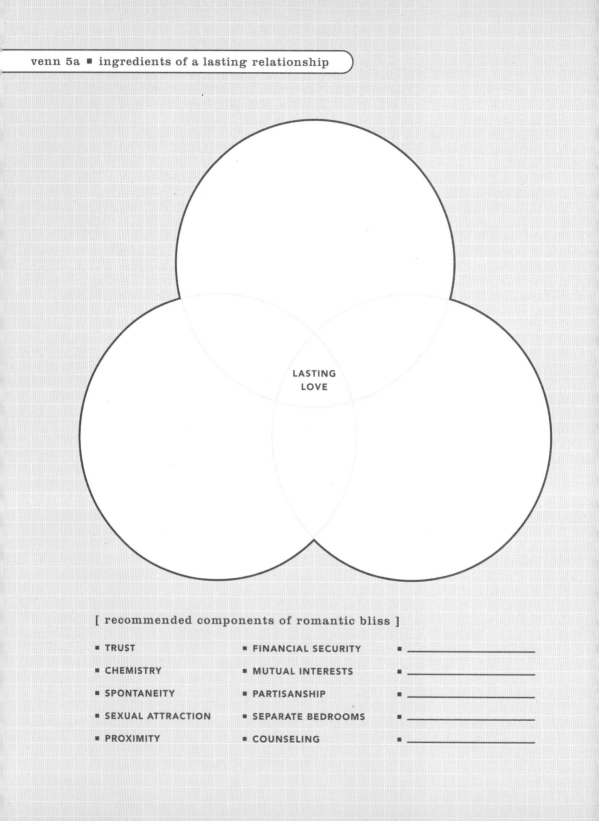

LASTING
LOVE

[recommended components of romantic bliss]

- TRUST
- CHEMISTRY
- SPONTANEITY
- SEXUAL ATTRACTION
- PROXIMITY

- FINANCIAL SECURITY
- MUTUAL INTERESTS
- PARTISANSHIP
- SEPARATE BEDROOMS
- COUNSELING

- _____
- _____
- _____
- _____
- _____

CLICHÉ #1: _____

ON SCREEN	IN LIFE

CLICHÉ #2: _____

ON SCREEN	IN LIFE

CLICHÉ #3: _____

ON SCREEN	IN LIFE

CLICHÉ #4: _____

ON SCREEN	IN LIFE

CLICHÉ #5: _____

ON SCREEN	IN LIFE

CLICHÉ #6: _____

ON SCREEN	IN LIFE

[stock scenarios to consider]

- STAR-CROSSED LOVE
- FAMILY STRIFE
- OVERCOMING ADVERSITY

- FOREIGN ESPIONAGE
- UNCERTAIN PARENTAGE
- CELEBRITY CAMEOS

- _____
- _____
- _____

- ☐ DRAMA
- ☐ COMEDY
- ☐ TRAGICOMEDY

- ☐ ROM-COM
- ☐ QUIRKY INDIE
- ☐ FOREIGN

- ☐ HORROR
- ☐ MUSICAL
- ☐ WESTERN

- ☐ THRILLER
- ☐ FRENCH NEW WAVE
- ☐ BIOGRAPHY

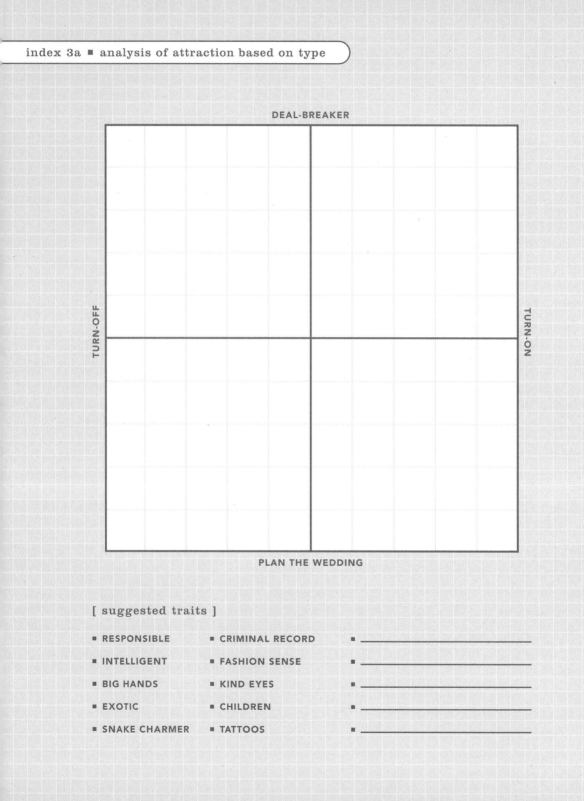

DEAL-BREAKER

TURN-OFF

TURN-ON

PLAN THE WEDDING

[suggested traits]

- RESPONSIBLE
- INTELLIGENT
- BIG HANDS
- EXOTIC
- SNAKE CHARMER

- CRIMINAL RECORD
- FASHION SENSE
- KIND EYES
- CHILDREN
- TATTOOS

- _____
- _____
- _____
- _____
- _____

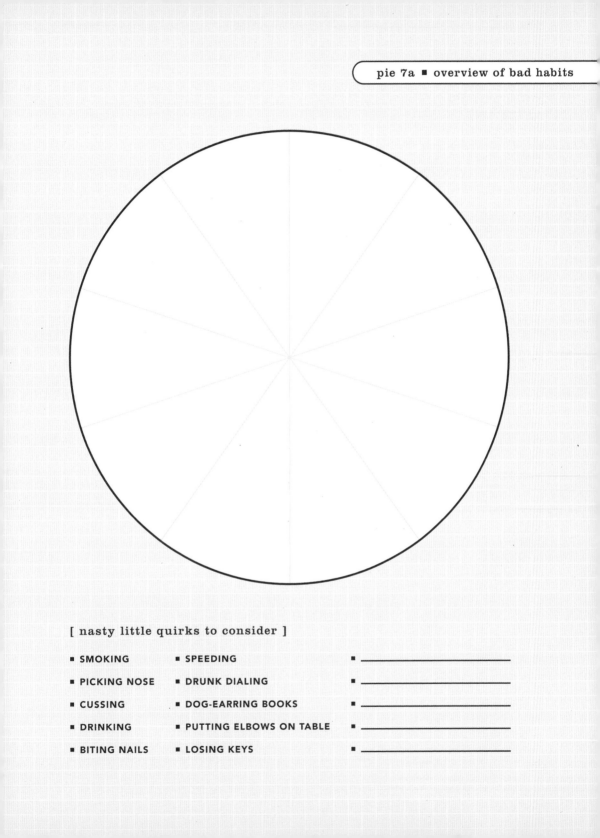

[nasty little quirks to consider]

- SMOKING
- PICKING NOSE
- CUSSING
- DRINKING
- BITING NAILS

- SPEEDING
- DRUNK DIALING
- DOG-EARRING BOOKS
- PUTTING ELBOWS ON TABLE
- LOSING KEYS

- _____
- _____
- _____
- _____
- _____

pyramid 1a ■ description of personal food habits

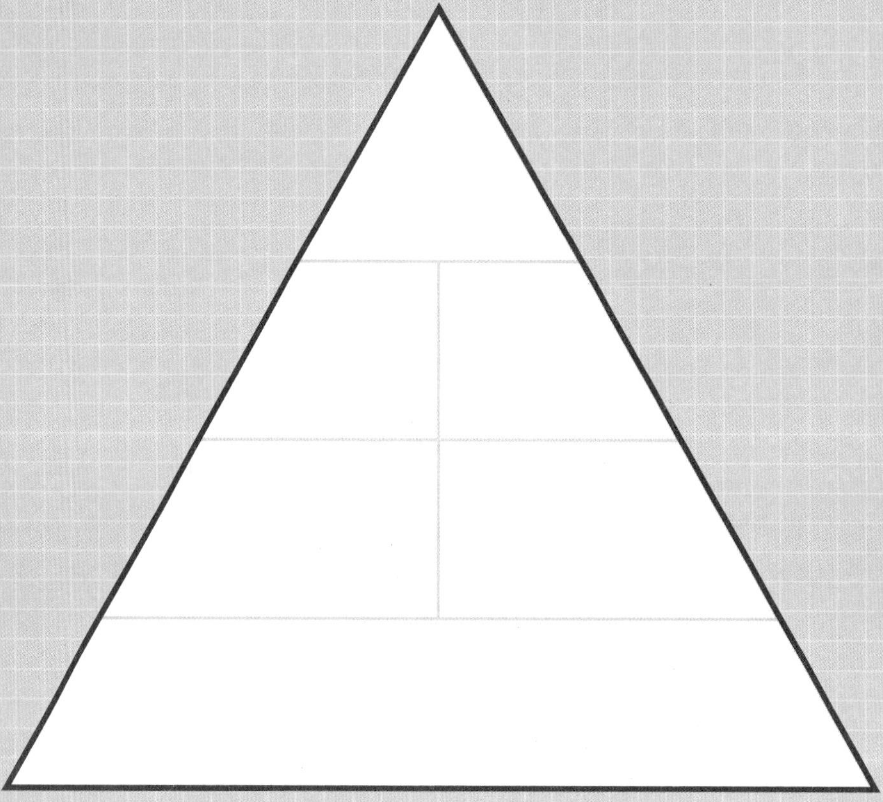

[suggested food groups]

■ MEATS	■ DAIRY	■ ________________
■ VEGETABLES	■ SWEETS	■ ________________
■ GRAINS	■ FRUITS	■ ________________
■ FATS	■ BURRITOS	■ ________________
■ FISH	■ CONDIMENTS	■ ________________

CONCLUSIONS BASED ON GRAPHIC EVIDENCE: ________________

____

____

RELATIVE #1: _____

RELATIVE #2: _____

[suggested characteristics]

▪ SUPPORTIVE

▪ LOVING

▪ INTRUSIVE

▪ CRITICAL

▪ MARTYR

▪ GENEROUS

▪ COMPETITIVE

▪ UNDERACHIEVER

▪ OVERACHIEVER

▪ BOSSY

▪ _____

▪ _____

▪ _____

▪ _____

▪ _____

RELATIVE #3: _____

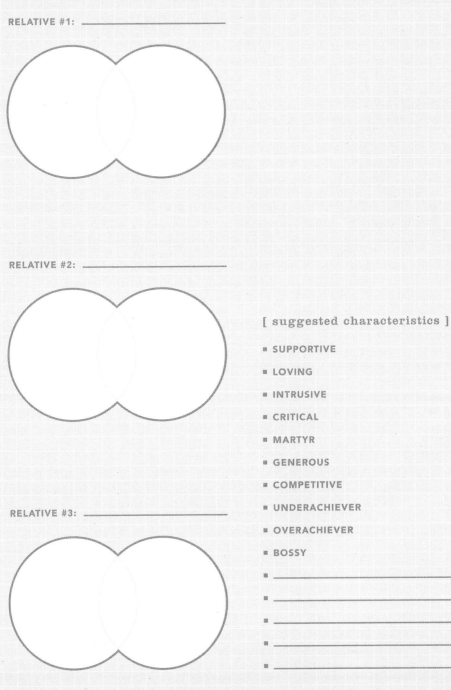

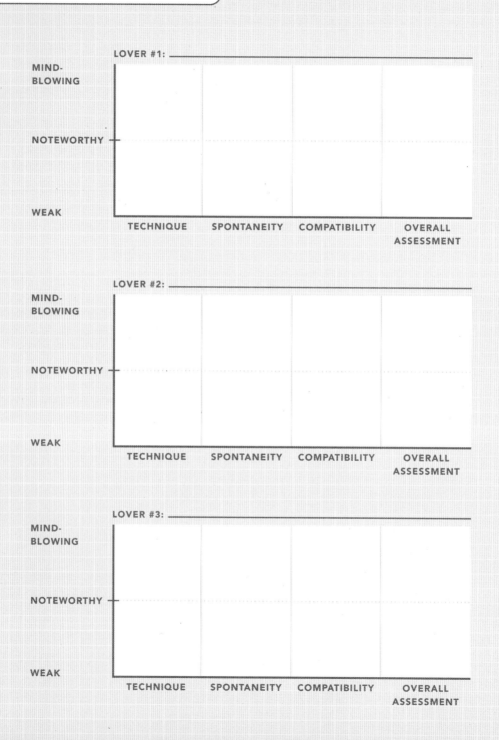

LOVER #1: _____

MIND-BLOWING

NOTEWORTHY

WEAK

TECHNIQUE   SPONTANEITY   COMPATIBILITY   OVERALL ASSESSMENT

LOVER #2: _____

MIND-BLOWING

NOTEWORTHY

WEAK

TECHNIQUE   SPONTANEITY   COMPATIBILITY   OVERALL ASSESSMENT

LOVER #3: _____

MIND-BLOWING

NOTEWORTHY

WEAK

TECHNIQUE   SPONTANEITY   COMPATIBILITY   OVERALL ASSESSMENT

pie 8a ■ principal causes of anger

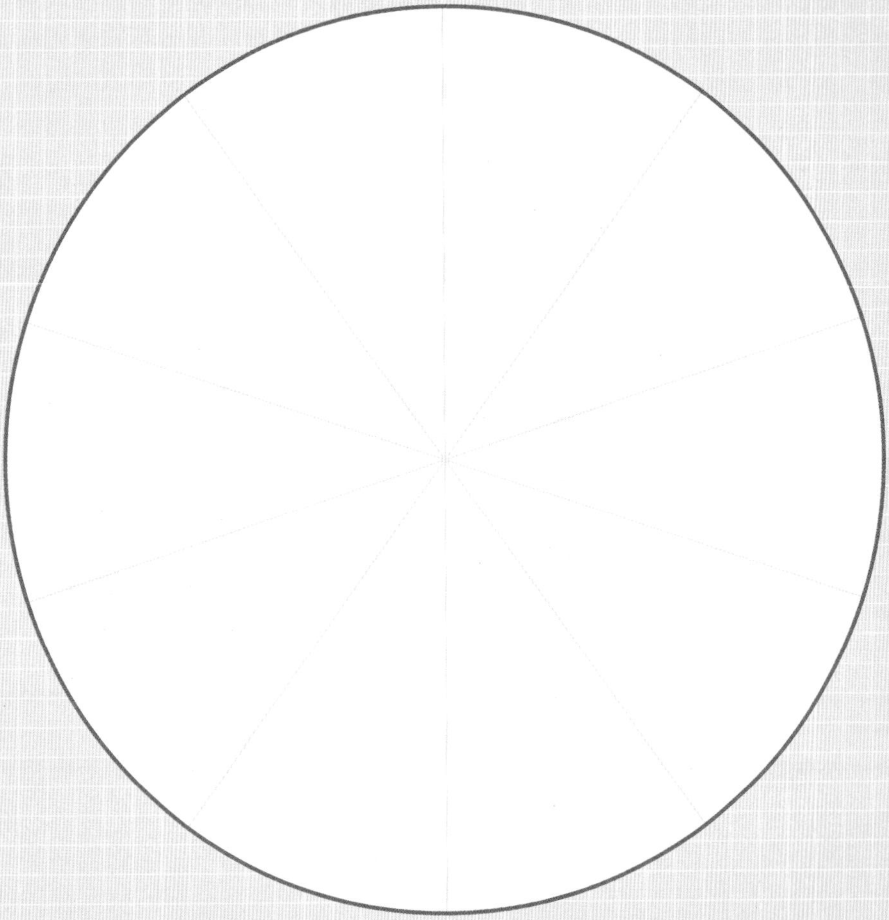

[possible sources of irritation]

- TRAFFIC
- WORK
- RELATIONSHIPS
- POLITICIANS
- FAMILY
- SOCIAL ISSUES
- PHONE SOLICITORS
- MONEY
- IDIOTS
- INANIMATE OBJECTS
- ______________________
- ______________________
- ______________________
- ______________________
- ______________________

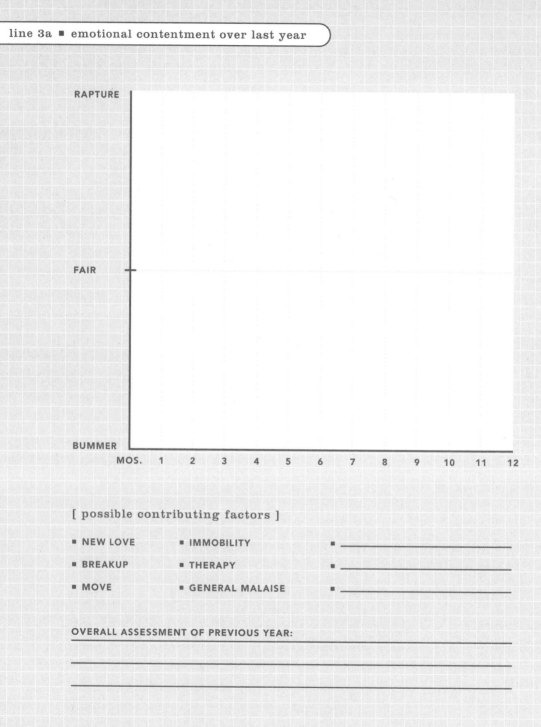

[possible contributing factors]

- NEW LOVE   ■ IMMOBILITY   ■ _____
- BREAKUP   ■ THERAPY   ■ _____
- MOVE   ■ GENERAL MALAISE   ■ _____

OVERALL ASSESSMENT OF PREVIOUS YEAR: _____
_____
_____

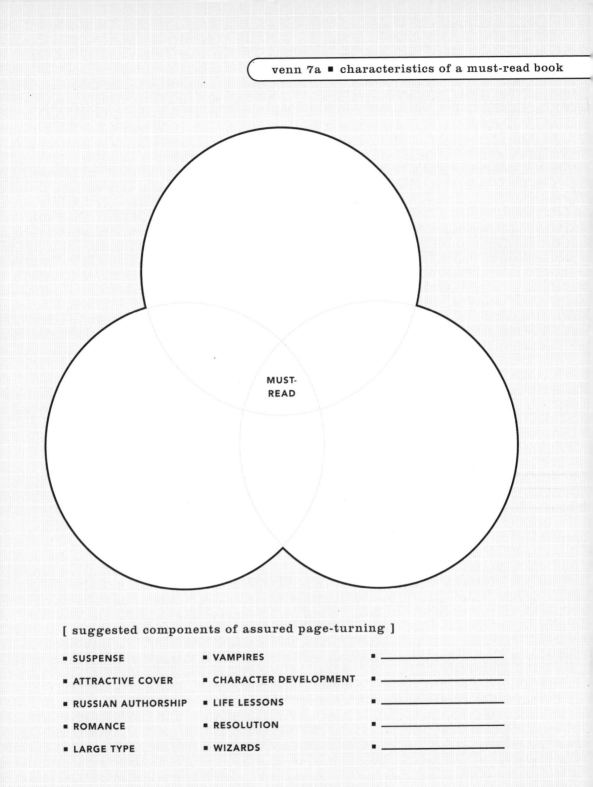

MUST-
READ

[suggested components of assured page-turning]

- SUSPENSE
- ATTRACTIVE COVER
- RUSSIAN AUTHORSHIP
- ROMANCE
- LARGE TYPE

- VAMPIRES
- CHARACTER DEVELOPMENT
- LIFE LESSONS
- RESOLUTION
- WIZARDS

- _____
- _____
- _____
- _____
- _____

[what you see]

☐ YOUR PARENTS   ☐ FISH   ☐ _____

☐ CAR WRECK   ☐ FIRE TRUCK   ☐ _____

☐ BUTTERFLY   ☐ EX-LOVER ON FIRE   ☐ _____

☐ SUNSET   ☐ GOD   ☐ _____

☐ LIGHTHOUSE   ☐ DEVIL   ☐ _____

PSYCHOLOGICAL BREAKTHROUGH: _____
_____
_____
_____

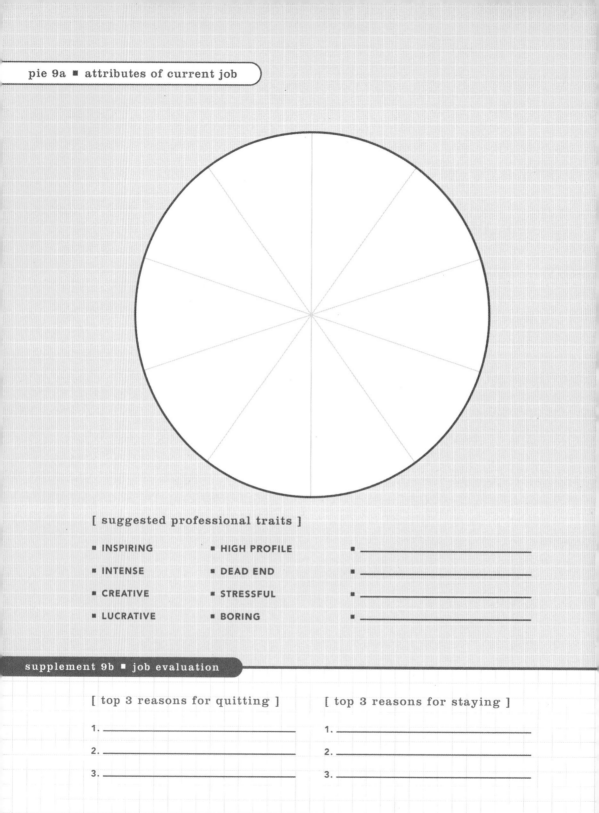

[suggested professional traits]

■ INSPIRING   ■ HIGH PROFILE   ■ _____

■ INTENSE   ■ DEAD END   ■ _____

■ CREATIVE   ■ STRESSFUL   ■ _____

■ LUCRATIVE   ■ BORING   ■ _____

supplement 9b ■ job evaluation

[top 3 reasons for quitting]   [top 3 reasons for staying]

1. _____   1. _____

2. _____   2. _____

3. _____   3. _____

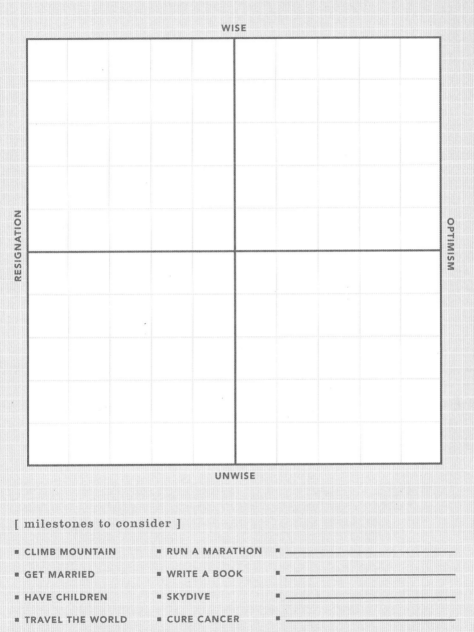

WISE

RESIGNATION

OPTIMISM

UNWISE

[milestones to consider]

- CLIMB MOUNTAIN   ▪ RUN A MARATHON   ▪ _____
- GET MARRIED   ▪ WRITE A BOOK   ▪ _____
- HAVE CHILDREN   ▪ SKYDIVE   ▪ _____
- TRAVEL THE WORLD ▪ CURE CANCER   ▪ _____
- MAKE PARENTS PROUD ▪ ACCEPT SELF   ▪ _____

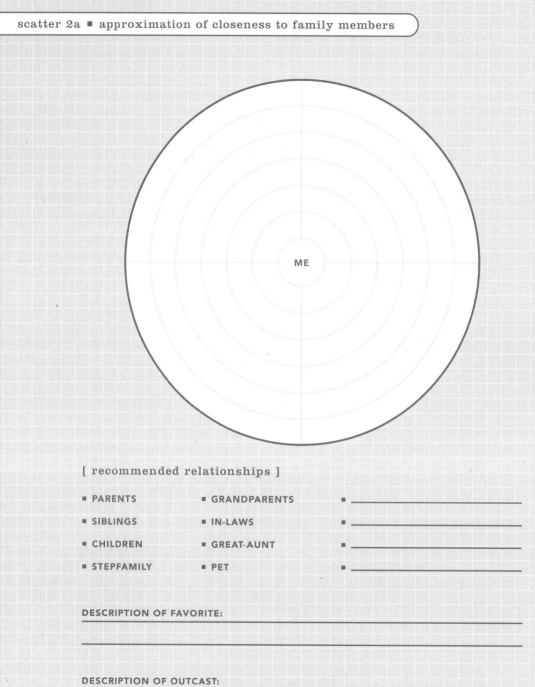

ME

[recommended relationships]

- PARENTS   ■ GRANDPARENTS   ■ _____

- SIBLINGS   ■ IN-LAWS   ■ _____

- CHILDREN   ■ GREAT-AUNT   ■ _____

- STEPFAMILY   ■ PET   ■ _____

DESCRIPTION OF FAVORITE: _____

_____

DESCRIPTION OF OUTCAST: _____

_____

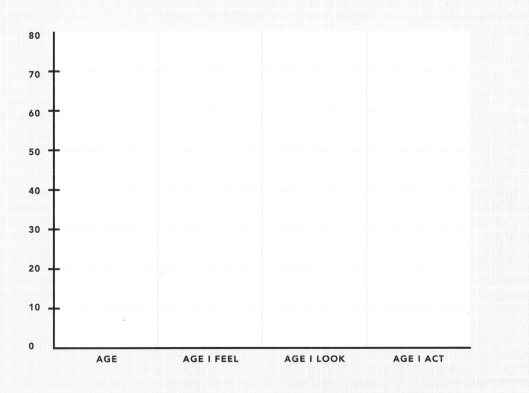

80
70
60
50
40
30
20
10
0

AGE   AGE I FEEL   AGE I LOOK   AGE I ACT

BENEFITS OF AGING: _____

_____

_____

DRAWBACKS OF AGING: _____

_____

_____

supplement 5b ■ number of years taken due to

- **STRESS:** _____   - **CHILDREN:** _____   - **GENETICS** _____
- **PARTYING:** _____   - **SUN:** _____   - **BACON:** _____

pie 10a ▪ breakdown of monthly spending

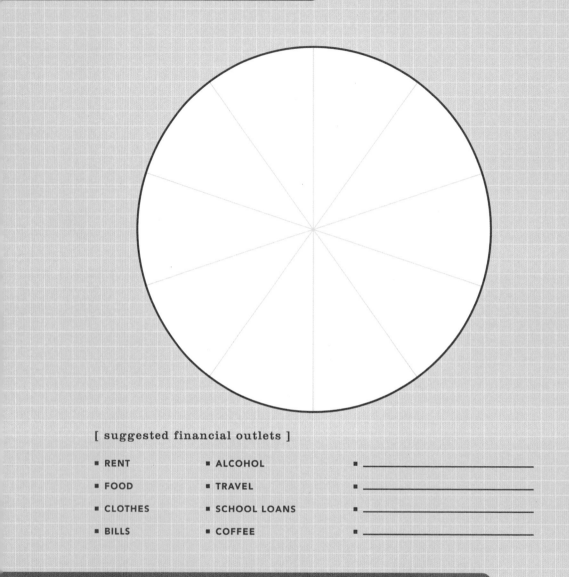

[suggested financial outlets]

- RENT
- FOOD
- CLOTHES
- BILLS

- ALCOHOL
- TRAVEL
- SCHOOL LOANS
- COFFEE

- _____
- _____
- _____
- _____

supplement 10b ▪ mathematical breakdown of the importance of thrift

[>, <, (or) =]

- DEBT _____ SPENDING MONEY
- DEBT _____ HUNGER
- DEBT _____ NEW CLOTHES

- DEBT _____ GOING OUT
- DEBT _____ SMART PHONE
- DEBT _____ PEACE OF MIND

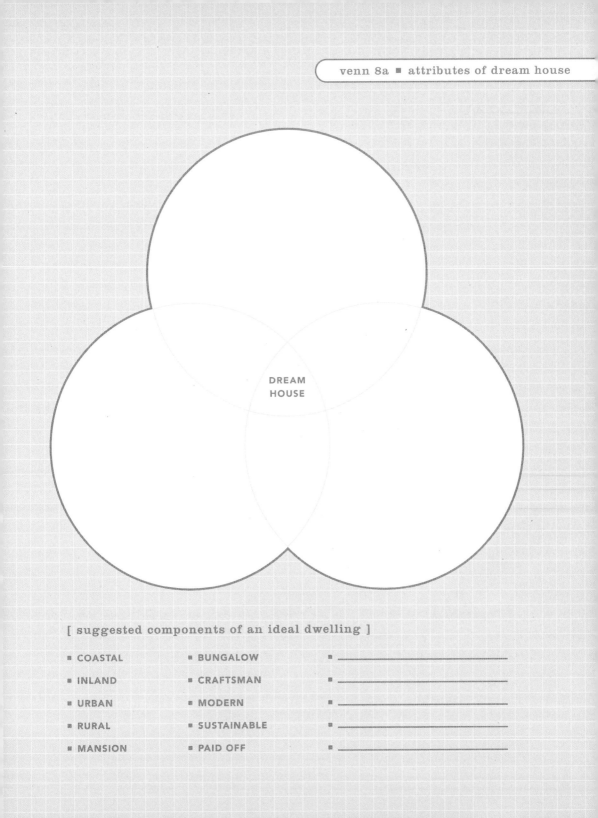

DREAM
HOUSE

[suggested components of an ideal dwelling]

- COASTAL
- INLAND
- URBAN
- RURAL
- MANSION

- BUNGALOW
- CRAFTSMAN
- MODERN
- SUSTAINABLE
- PAID OFF

- _____
- _____
- _____
- _____
- _____

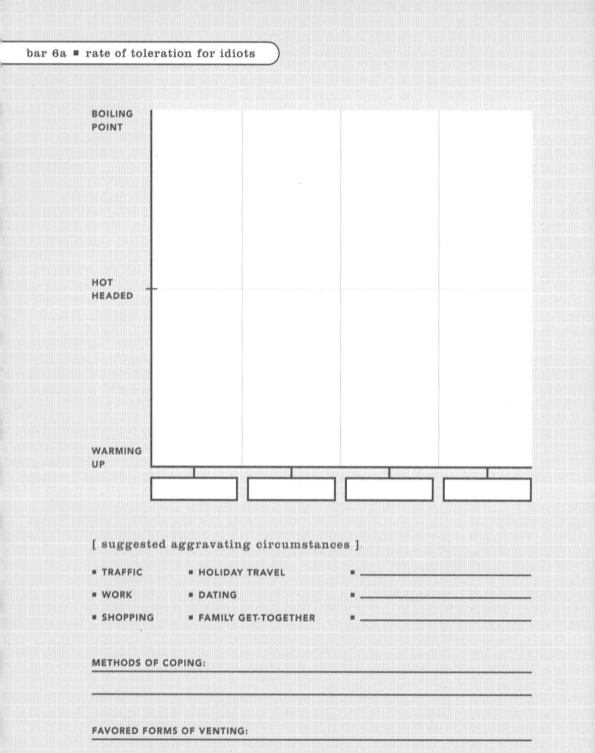

BOILING
POINT

HOT
HEADED

WARMING
UP

[suggested aggravating circumstances]

- TRAFFIC   - HOLIDAY TRAVEL   - _____

- WORK   - DATING   - _____

- SHOPPING   - FAMILY GET-TOGETHER   - _____

METHODS OF COPING:
_____
_____

FAVORED FORMS OF VENTING:
_____
_____

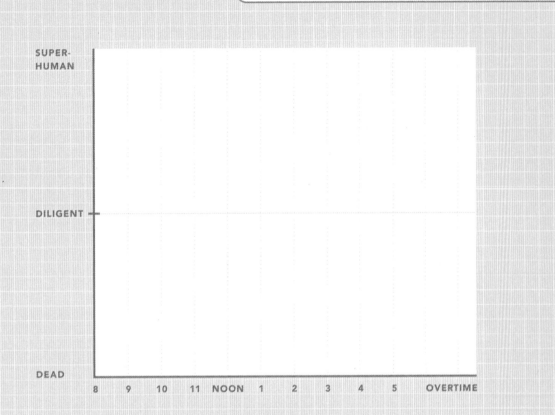

SUPER-
HUMAN

DILIGENT —

DEAD

8   9   10   11   NOON   1   2   3   4   5   OVERTIME

REPEATING FACTORS THAT AFFECT OUTPUT:

_____

_____

_____

[favored stimulants]

☐ COFFEE   ☐ NAP UNDER DESK   ☐ JUMPING JACKS

☐ YOGA   ☐ HERBAL TEA   ☐ COMPLAINING

☐ SMOKE BREAK   ☐ TRAIL MIX   ☐ "EYE OF THE TIGER"

☐ ENERGY DRINK   ☐ SURFING INTERNET   ☐ RITALIN

INDIVIDUAL #1: _____

COOL		NOT COOL

INDIVIDUAL #2: _____

COOL		NOT COOL

INDIVIDUAL #3: _____

COOL		NOT COOL

INDIVIDUAL #4: _____

COOL		NOT COOL

INDIVIDUAL #5: _____

COOL		NOT COOL

[suggested barometers of cool]

▪ YOU   ▪ BOSS   ▪ _____

▪ BEST FRIEND ▪ COWORKER   ▪ _____

▪ PARENTS   ▪ HIPSTER BARISTA   ▪ _____

supplement 3b ▪ distribution of cool points

[-10 to +10]

▪ TATTOO: _____   ▪ BACKSTAGE PASSES: _____

▪ MOTORCYCLE: _____   ▪ COMFORT IN SKIN: _____

▪ ROAD BIKE: _____   ▪ IRONY DEPLOYMENT: _____

▪ ESOTERIC MUSICAL TASTE: _____   ▪ PRIVATE JET: _____

▪ INSOUCIANCE: _____   ▪ COMIC BOOK COLLECTION: _____

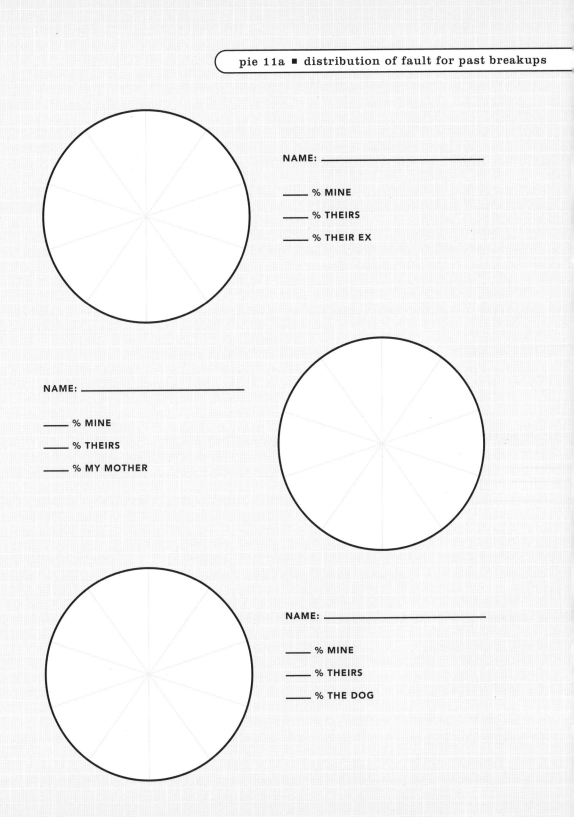

NAME: _____

_____ % MINE

_____ % THEIRS

_____ % THEIR EX

NAME: _____

_____ % MINE

_____ % THEIRS

_____ % MY MOTHER

NAME: _____

_____ % MINE

_____ % THEIRS

_____ % THE DOG

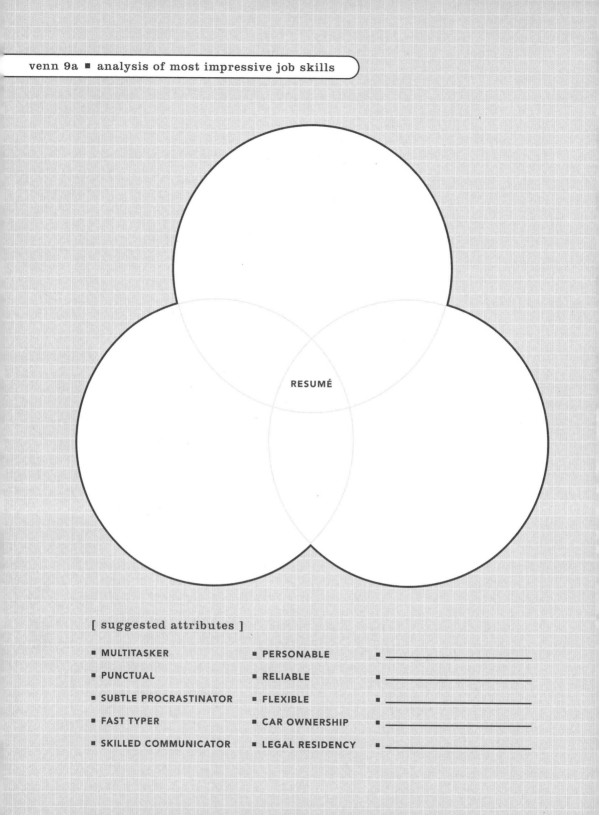

RESUMÉ

[suggested attributes]

■ MULTITASKER   ■ PERSONABLE   ■ _____

■ PUNCTUAL   ■ RELIABLE   ■ _____

■ SUBTLE PROCRASTINATOR ■ FLEXIBLE   ■ _____

■ FAST TYPER   ■ CAR OWNERSHIP   ■ _____

■ SKILLED COMMUNICATOR ■ LEGAL RESIDENCY   ■ _____

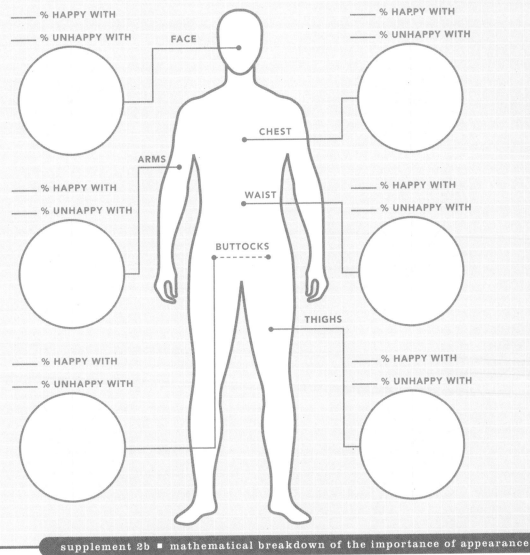

_____ % HAPPY WITH

_____ % UNHAPPY WITH   FACE

_____ % HAPPY WITH

_____ % UNHAPPY WITH

CHEST

ARMS

_____ % HAPPY WITH

_____ % UNHAPPY WITH

WAIST

_____ % HAPPY WITH

_____ % UNHAPPY WITH

BUTTOCKS

THIGHS

_____ % HAPPY WITH

_____ % UNHAPPY WITH

_____ % HAPPY WITH

_____ % UNHAPPY WITH

supplement 2b ■ mathematical breakdown of the importance of appearance

[>, <, (or) =]

- BEAUTY _____ HEALTH
- BEAUTY _____ HAPPINESS
- BEAUTY _____ WEALTH

- BEAUTY _____ SUCCESS
- BEAUTY _____ INTELLIGENCE
- BEAUTY _____ RESPECT

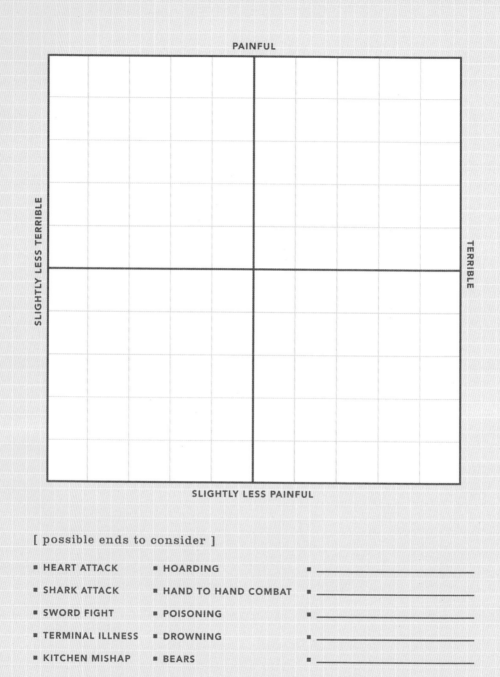

PAINFUL

SLIGHTLY LESS TERRIBLE

TERRIBLE

SLIGHTLY LESS PAINFUL

[possible ends to consider]

■ HEART ATTACK   ■ HOARDING   ■ _____

■ SHARK ATTACK   ■ HAND TO HAND COMBAT   ■ _____

■ SWORD FIGHT   ■ POISONING   ■ _____

■ TERMINAL ILLNESS   ■ DROWNING   ■ _____

■ KITCHEN MISHAP   ■ BEARS   ■ _____

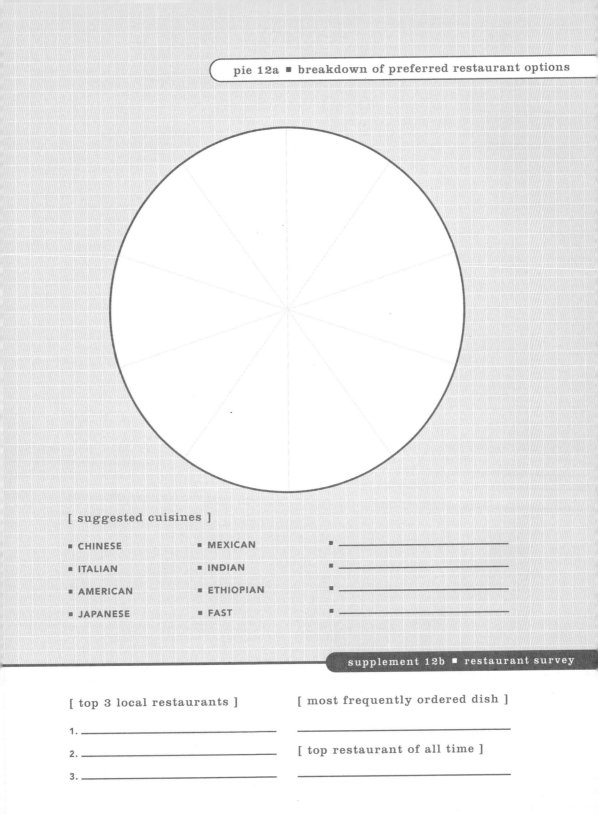

[suggested cuisines]

- CHINESE
- ITALIAN
- AMERICAN
- JAPANESE

- MEXICAN
- INDIAN
- ETHIOPIAN
- FAST

- _____
- _____
- _____
- _____

supplement 12b ■ restaurant survey

[top 3 local restaurants]

1. _____
2. _____
3. _____

[most frequently ordered dish]

_____

[top restaurant of all time]

_____

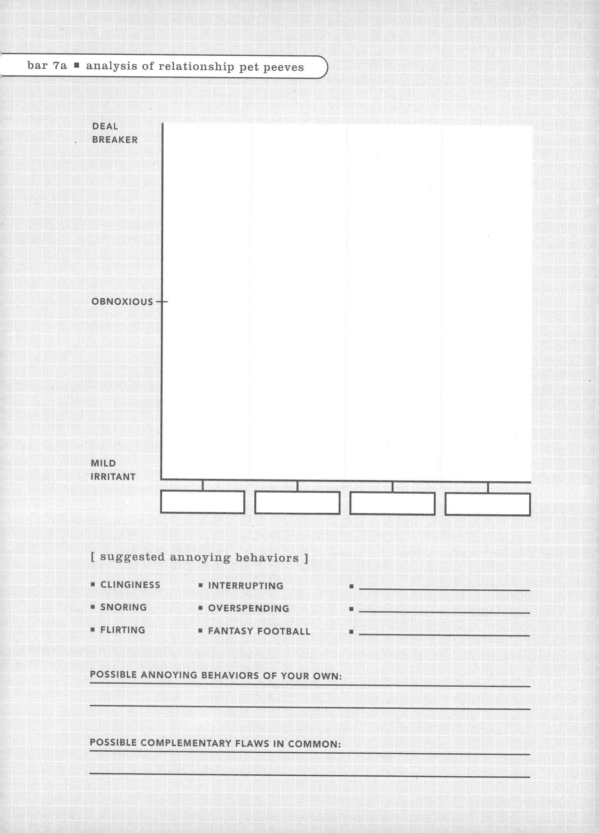

DEAL
BREAKER

OBNOXIOUS —

MILD
IRRITANT

[suggested annoying behaviors]

- CLINGINESS   - INTERRUPTING   - _____

- SNORING   - OVERSPENDING   - _____

- FLIRTING   - FANTASY FOOTBALL - _____

POSSIBLE ANNOYING BEHAVIORS OF YOUR OWN:

_____

_____

POSSIBLE COMPLEMENTARY FLAWS IN COMMON:

_____

_____

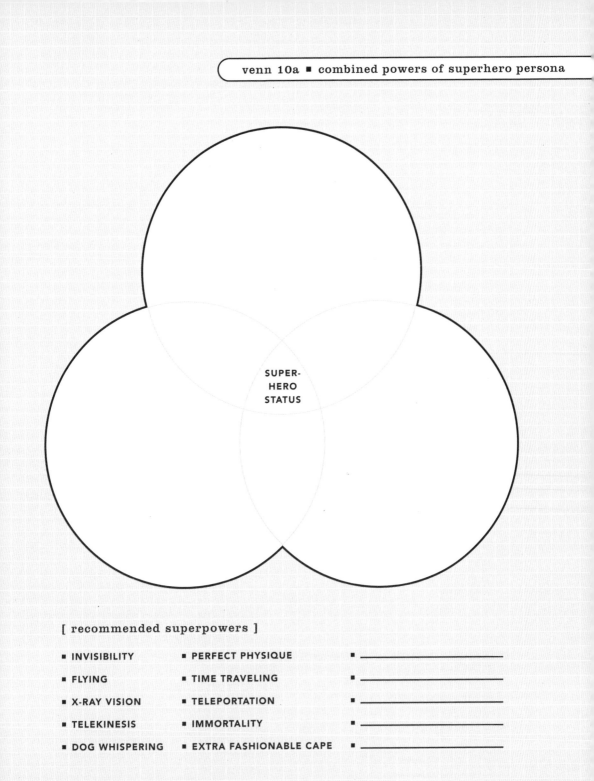

SUPER-
HERO
STATUS

[recommended superpowers]

- INVISIBILITY
- FLYING
- X-RAY VISION
- TELEKINESIS
- DOG WHISPERING

- PERFECT PHYSIQUE
- TIME TRAVELING
- TELEPORTATION
- IMMORTALITY
- EXTRA FASHIONABLE CAPE

- _____
- _____
- _____
- _____
- _____

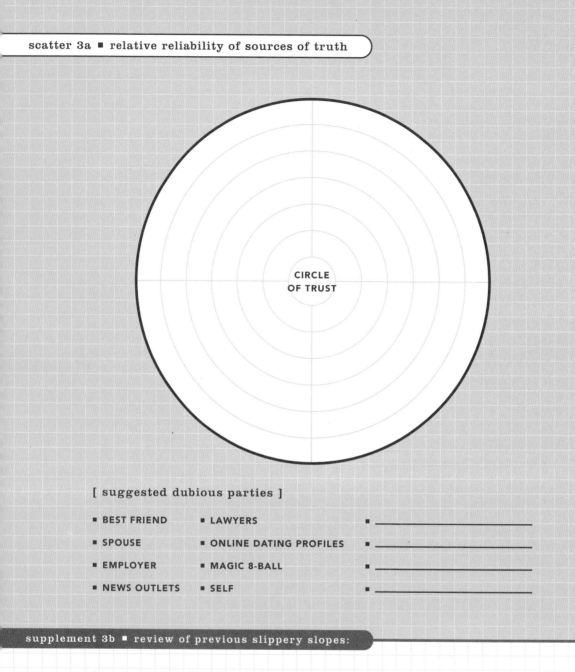

CIRCLE
OF TRUST

[suggested dubious parties]

- BEST FRIEND
- SPOUSE
- EMPLOYER
- NEWS OUTLETS

- LAWYERS
- ONLINE DATING PROFILES
- MAGIC 8-BALL
- SELF

- _____
- _____
- _____
- _____

supplement 3b ■ review of previous slippery slopes:

[instance in which you wish you had been deceived]

_____

[instance in which you are grateful for dishonesty]

_____

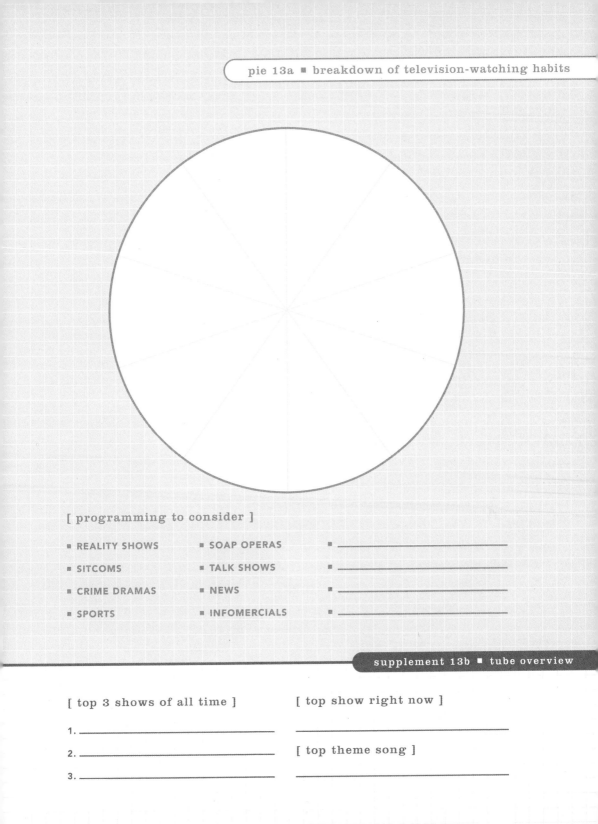

[programming to consider]

- REALITY SHOWS
- SITCOMS
- CRIME DRAMAS
- SPORTS

- SOAP OPERAS
- TALK SHOWS
- NEWS
- INFOMERCIALS

- _____
- _____
- _____
- _____

supplement 13b ■ tube overview

[top 3 shows of all time]

1. _____
2. _____
3. _____

[top show right now]

_____

[top theme song]

_____

instructions:
[fill in states that you have been to—flight connections don't count]

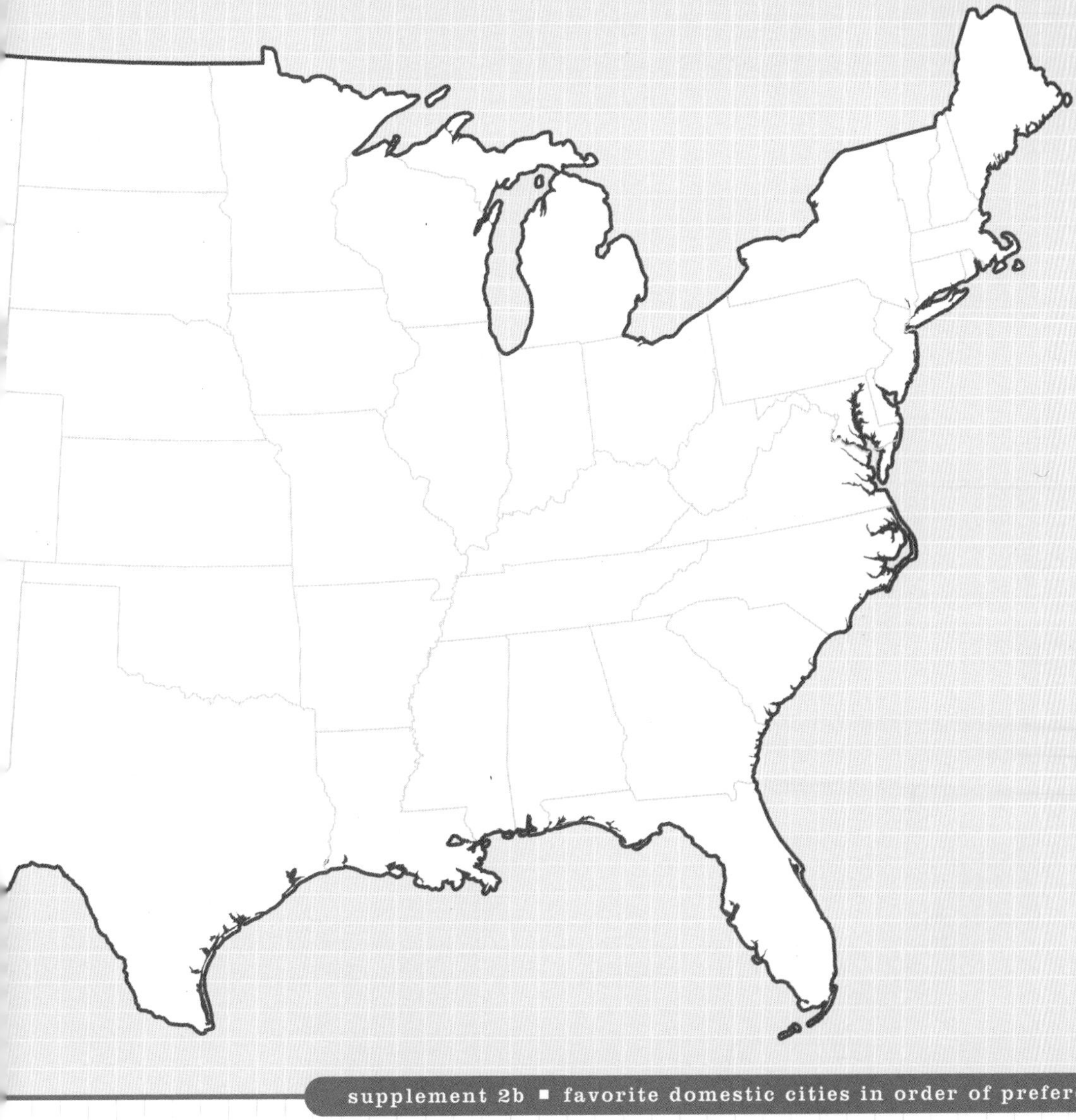

supplement 2b ■ favorite domestic cities in order of preference

[favored destinations]

1. ______________________

2. ______________________

3. ______________________

[most visited]

____

[times visited]

____

instructions:
[fill in countries that you have been to—flight connections don't count]

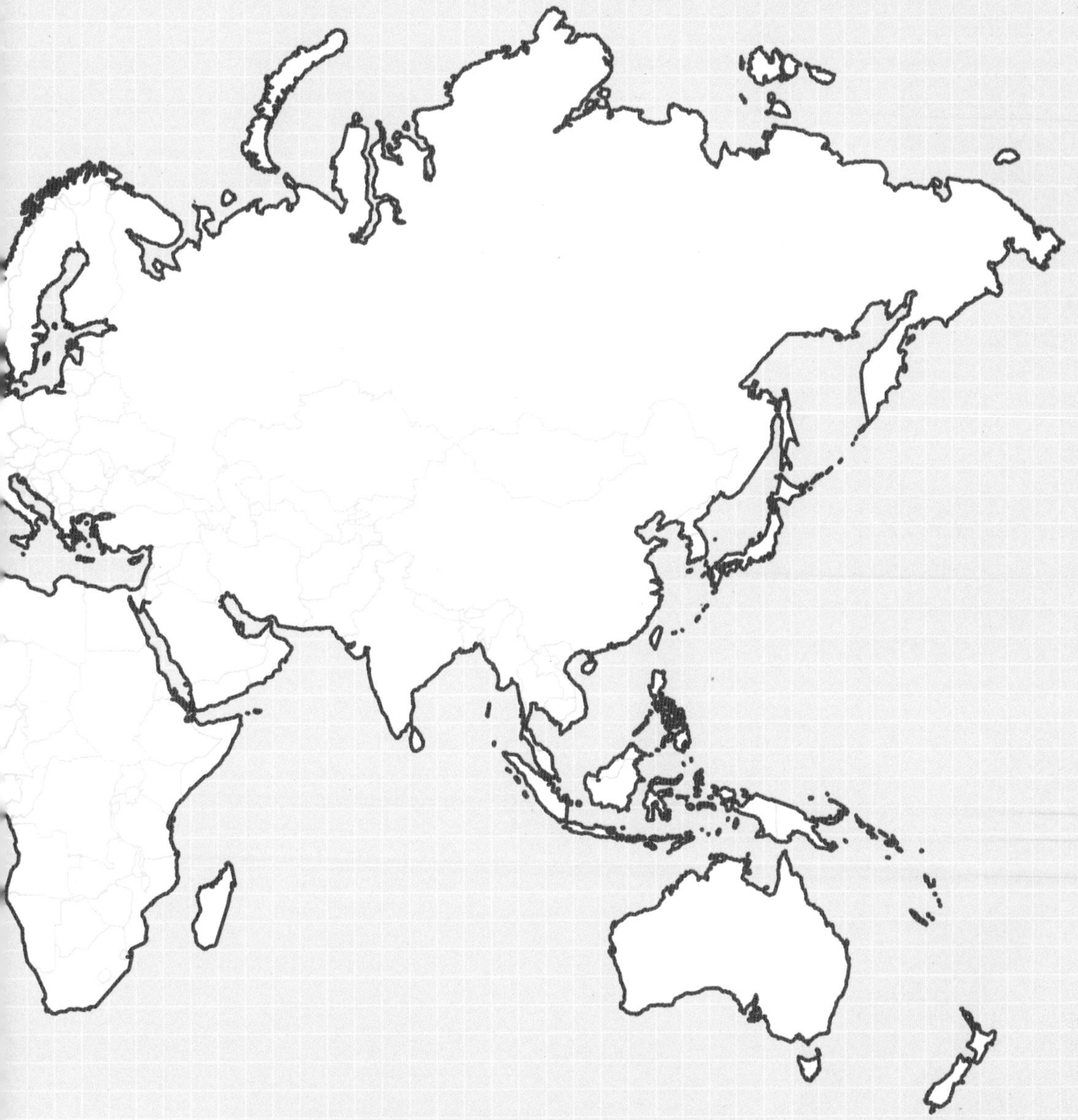

supplement 3b ▪ favorite international cities in order of preference

[favored destinations]

1. ______________________

2. ______________________

3. ______________________

[most visited]

____

[times visited]

____

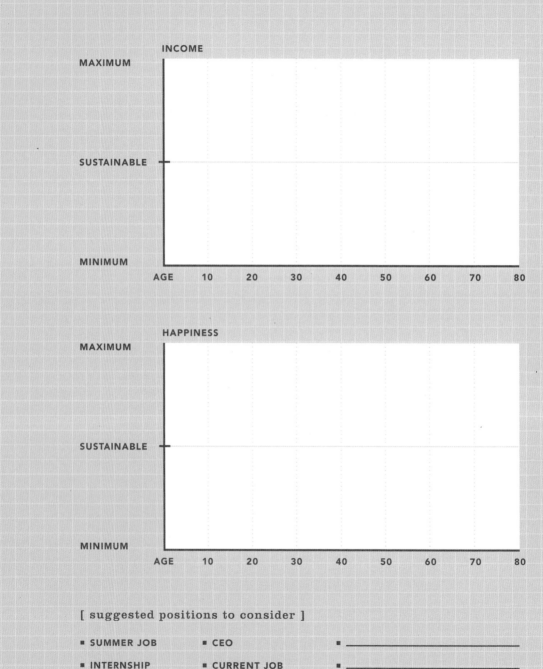

INCOME

MAXIMUM

SUSTAINABLE

MINIMUM

AGE   10   20   30   40   50   60   70   80

HAPPINESS

MAXIMUM

SUSTAINABLE

MINIMUM

AGE   10   20   30   40   50   60   70   80

[suggested positions to consider]

■ SUMMER JOB   ■ CEO   ■ _____

■ INTERNSHIP   ■ CURRENT JOB   ■ _____

■ ASSISTANT   ■ UNEMPLOYMENT   ■ _____

pie 14a ■ breakdown of beverage consumption

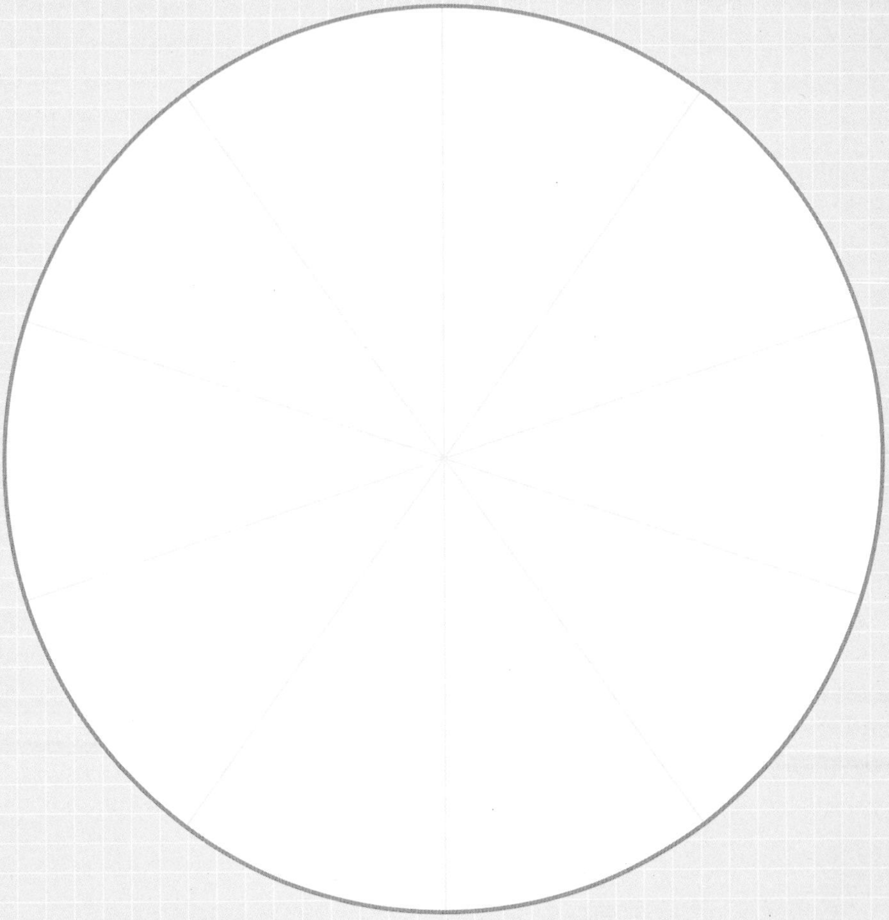

[suggested refreshments]

- WATER
- JUICE
- COFFEE
- WINE
- BEER
- STRAIGHT BOOZE
- DRINKS WITH UMBRELLAS
- POWDERED CONCOCTIONS
- SODA
- FRAPPUCCINOS™
- ______________________
- ______________________
- ______________________
- ______________________
- ______________________

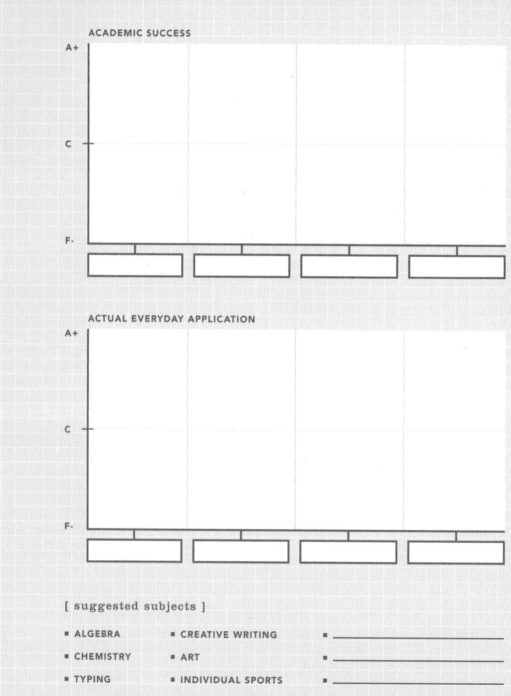

ACADEMIC SUCCESS

A+

C

F-

ACTUAL EVERYDAY APPLICATION

A+

C

F-

[suggested subjects]

■ ALGEBRA   ■ CREATIVE WRITING   ■ _____

■ CHEMISTRY   ■ ART   ■ _____

■ TYPING   ■ INDIVIDUAL SPORTS   ■ _____

index 6a ■ appraisal of potential career paths

SOUNDS FUN
EASY
HARD
SOUNDS BORING

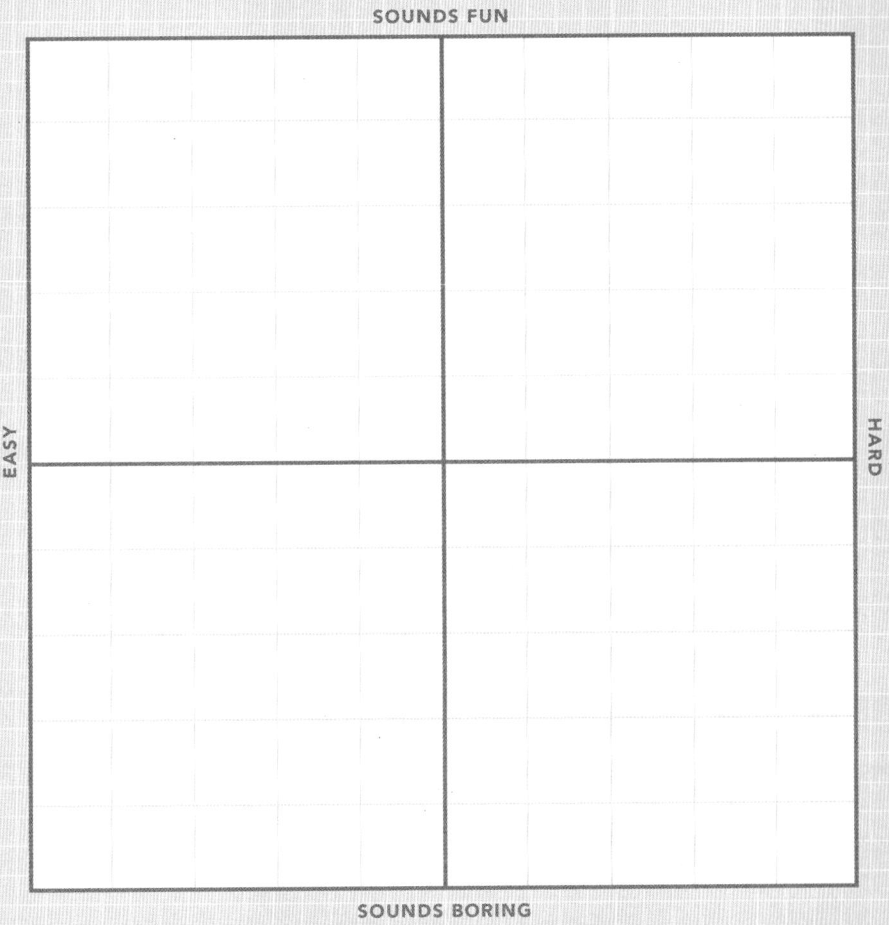

[suggested vocations]

- DOCTOR
- LAWYER
- ARTIST
- ROCK STAR
- GOLFER
- CAMP COUNSELOR
- NEWS ANCHOR
- TEACHER
- ACCOUNTANT
- GURU
- ______________________
- ______________________
- ______________________
- ______________________
- ______________________

pie 15a ■ distribution of creative outlets

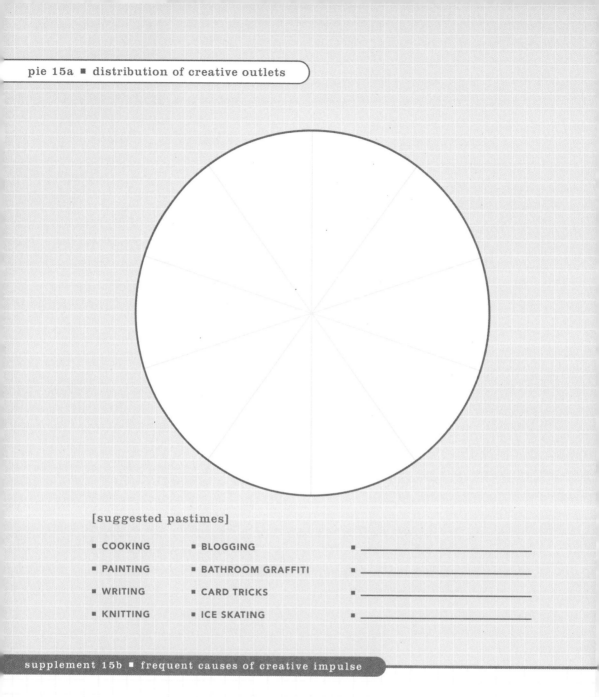

[suggested pastimes]

- COOKING
- PAINTING
- WRITING
- KNITTING

- BLOGGING
- BATHROOM GRAFFITI
- CARD TRICKS
- ICE SKATING

- _____
- _____
- _____
- _____

supplement 15b ■ frequent causes of creative impulse

☐ BOREDOM
☐ ANGST
☐ LACK OF MONEY

☐ IDENTITY AFFIRMATION
☐ EPIPHANY
☐ HOLIDAYS

☐ PROVING SOMETHING
☐ NEW SUPPLIES
☐ ACTUAL TALENT

PARTNER #1: _____

LUST	LOVE

PARTNER #2: _____

LUST	LOVE

PARTNER #3: _____

LUST	LOVE

PARTNER #4: _____

LUST	LOVE

PARTNER #5: _____

LUST	LOVE

PARTNER #6: _____

LUST	LOVE

PARTNER #7: _____

LUST	LOVE

supplement 4b ■ frequently recurring needs

☐ SENSITIVITY   ☐ RENT CONTRIBUTION   ☐ BELITTLEMENT

☐ AFFECTION   ☐ GUARANTEED PLUS-ONE   ☐ KISSES

☐ APPROVAL   ☐ PASSION   ☐ GIFTS

☐ SECURITY   ☐ GRATITUDE   ☐ FLATTERY

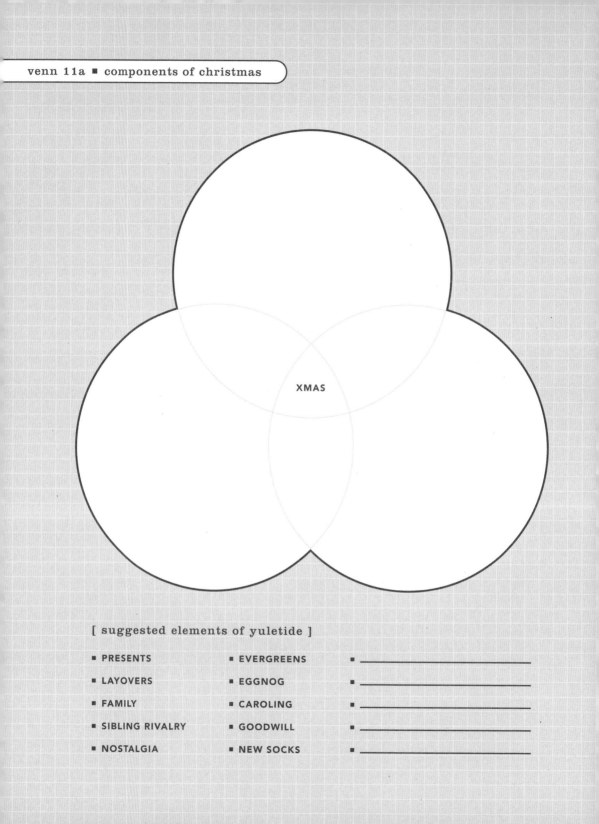

XMAS

[suggested elements of yuletide]

▪ PRESENTS   ▪ EVERGREENS   ▪ _____

▪ LAYOVERS   ▪ EGGNOG   ▪ _____

▪ FAMILY   ▪ CAROLING   ▪ _____

▪ SIBLING RIVALRY   ▪ GOODWILL   ▪ _____

▪ NOSTALGIA   ▪ NEW SOCKS   ▪ _____

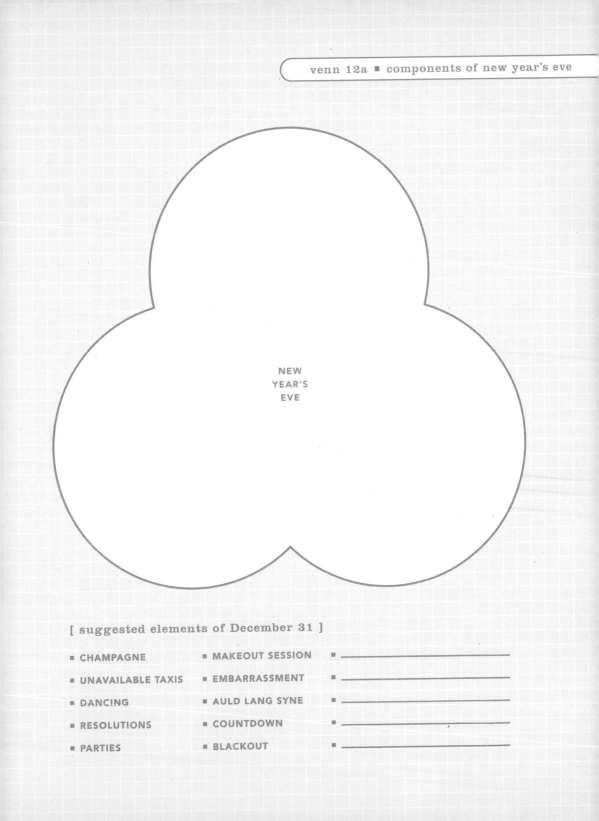

NEW
YEAR'S
EVE

[suggested elements of December 31]

■ CHAMPAGNE   ■ MAKEOUT SESSION   ■ _____

■ UNAVAILABLE TAXIS ■ EMBARRASSMENT   ■ _____

■ DANCING   ■ AULD LANG SYNE   ■ _____

■ RESOLUTIONS   ■ COUNTDOWN   ■ _____

■ PARTIES   ■ BLACKOUT   ■ _____

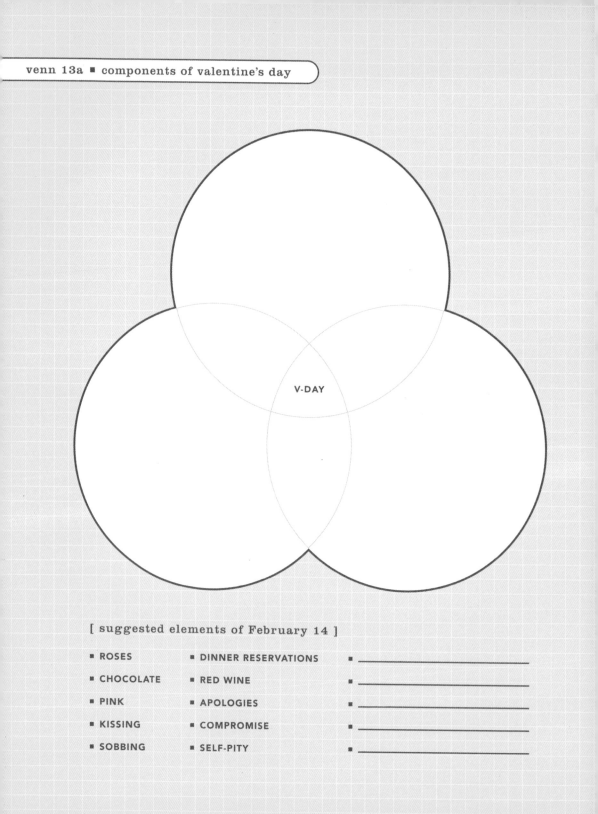

V-DAY

[suggested elements of February 14]

- ROSES
- CHOCOLATE
- PINK
- KISSING
- SOBBING

- DINNER RESERVATIONS
- RED WINE
- APOLOGIES
- COMPROMISE
- SELF-PITY

- _____
- _____
- _____
- _____
- _____

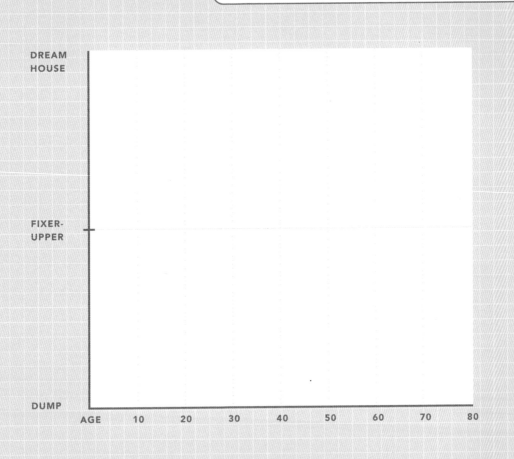

[milestones to consider]

▪ PARENTS' PLACE   ▪ FIRST APARTMENT   ▪ _____

▪ DORM   ▪ STARTER HOUSE   ▪ _____

▪ COLLEGE FLOPHOUSE   ▪ CURRENT DOMICILE   ▪ _____

ASSESSMENT OF COMFORTABLE LIVING SPACE VS. LOCATION: _____

_____

_____

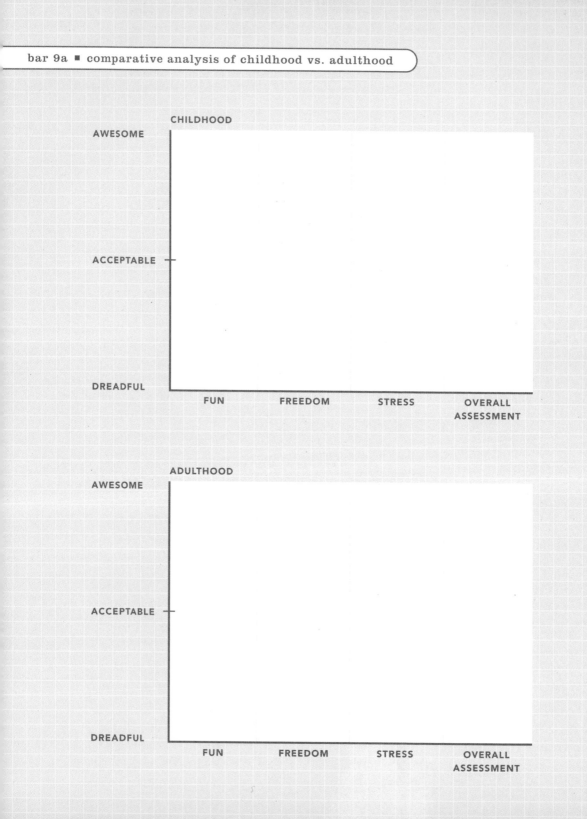

bar 9a ■ comparative analysis of childhood vs. adulthood

CHILDHOOD

AWESOME

ACCEPTABLE ─┼

DREADFUL

FUN   FREEDOM   STRESS   OVERALL
                                 ASSESSMENT

ADULTHOOD

AWESOME

ACCEPTABLE ─┼

DREADFUL

FUN   FREEDOM   STRESS   OVERALL
                                 ASSESSMENT

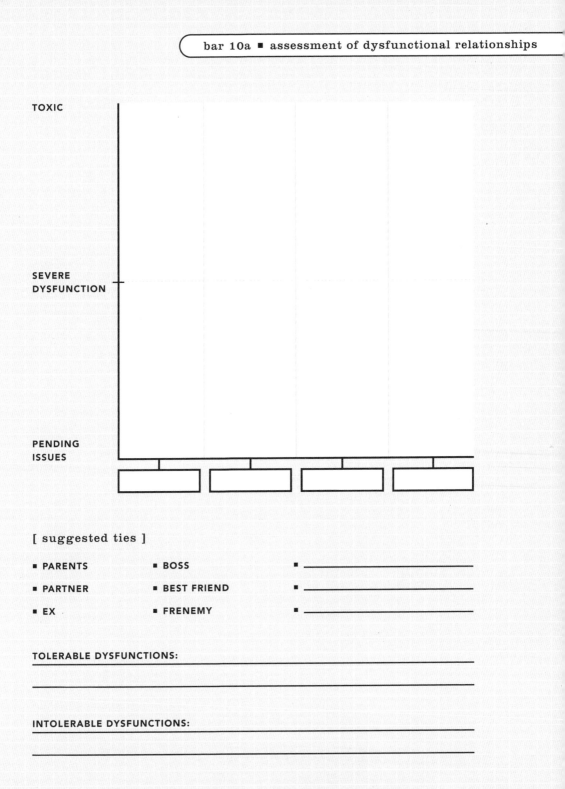

TOXIC

SEVERE
DYSFUNCTION

PENDING
ISSUES

[suggested ties]

- PARENTS
- PARTNER
- EX

- BOSS
- BEST FRIEND
- FRENEMY

- _____
- _____
- _____

TOLERABLE DYSFUNCTIONS:

_____

_____

INTOLERABLE DYSFUNCTIONS:

_____

_____

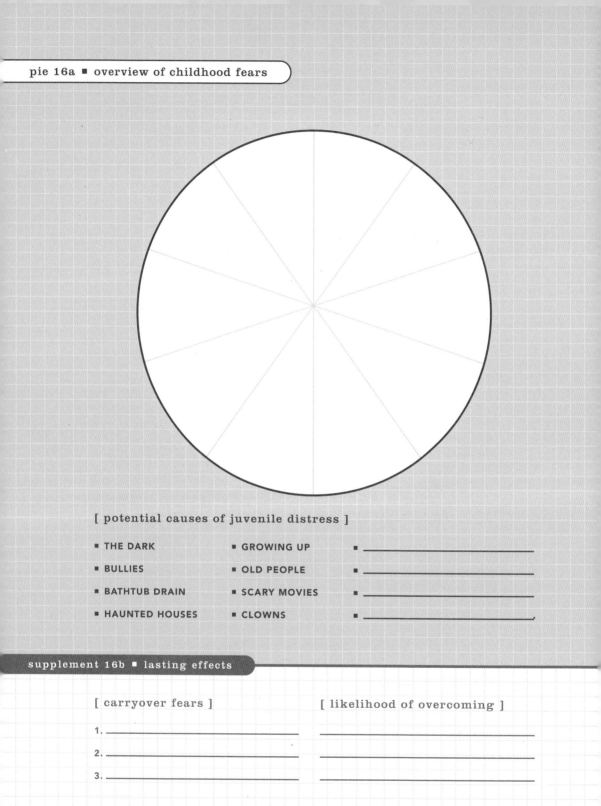

[potential causes of juvenile distress]

- THE DARK
- BULLIES
- BATHTUB DRAIN
- HAUNTED HOUSES

- GROWING UP
- OLD PEOPLE
- SCARY MOVIES
- CLOWNS

- _____
- _____
- _____
- _____

supplement 16b ■ lasting effects

[carryover fears]

1. _____
2. _____
3. _____

[likelihood of overcoming]

_____
_____
_____

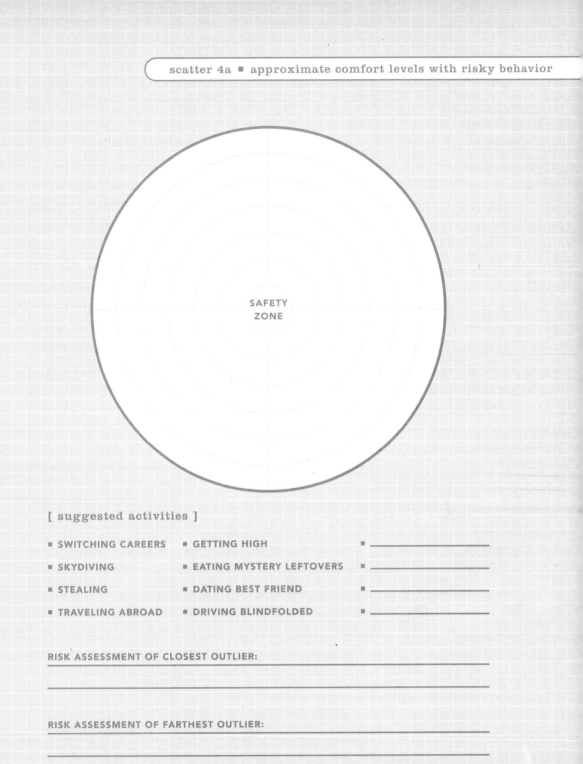

SAFETY
ZONE

[suggested activities]

■ SWITCHING CAREERS ■ GETTING HIGH ■ _____

■ SKYDIVING ■ EATING MYSTERY LEFTOVERS ■ _____

■ STEALING ■ DATING BEST FRIEND ■ _____

■ TRAVELING ABROAD ■ DRIVING BLINDFOLDED ■ _____

RISK ASSESSMENT OF CLOSEST OUTLIER: _____
_____

RISK ASSESSMENT OF FARTHEST OUTLIER: _____
_____

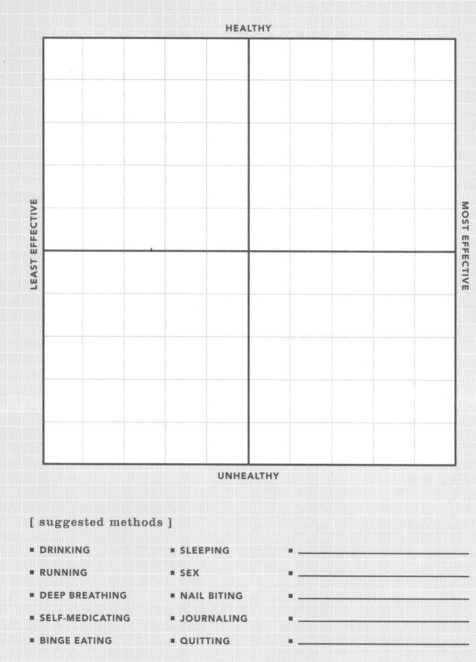

HEALTHY

LEAST EFFECTIVE

MOST EFFECTIVE

UNHEALTHY

[suggested methods]

- DRINKING
- RUNNING
- DEEP BREATHING
- SELF-MEDICATING
- BINGE EATING

- SLEEPING
- SEX
- NAIL BITING
- JOURNALING
- QUITTING

- _____
- _____
- _____
- _____
- _____

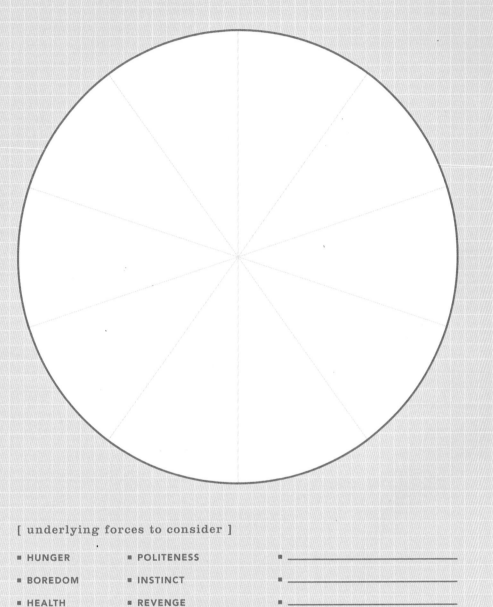

[underlying forces to consider]

■ HUNGER   ■ POLITENESS   ■ _____

■ BOREDOM   ■ INSTINCT   ■ _____

■ HEALTH   ■ REVENGE   ■ _____

■ CRAVING   ■ FILLING THE VOID   ■ _____

■ HABIT   ■ PROXIMITY   ■ _____

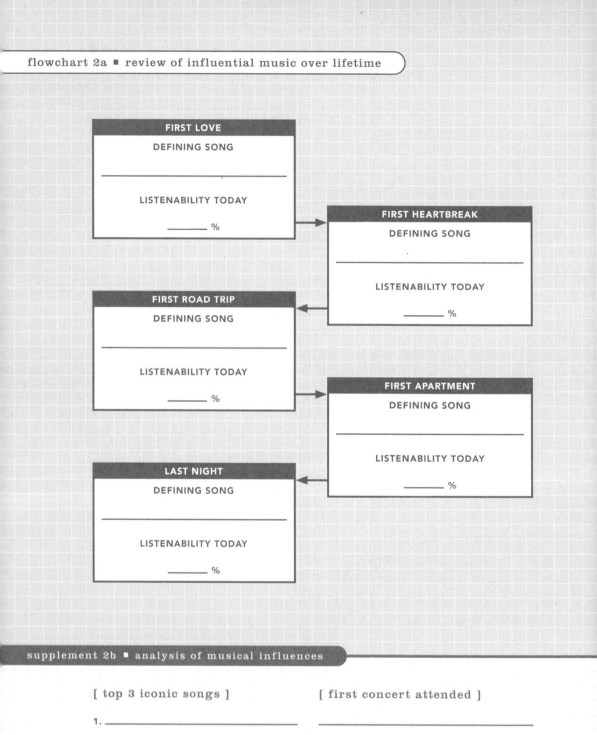

FIRST LOVE

DEFINING SONG

_____

LISTENABILITY TODAY

_____ %

FIRST HEARTBREAK

DEFINING SONG

_____

LISTENABILITY TODAY

_____ %

FIRST ROAD TRIP

DEFINING SONG

_____

LISTENABILITY TODAY

_____ %

FIRST APARTMENT

DEFINING SONG

_____

LISTENABILITY TODAY

_____ %

LAST NIGHT

DEFINING SONG

_____

LISTENABILITY TODAY

_____ %

supplement 2b ■ analysis of musical influences

[top 3 iconic songs]

1. _____

2. _____

3. _____

[first concert attended]

_____

[best concert attended]

_____

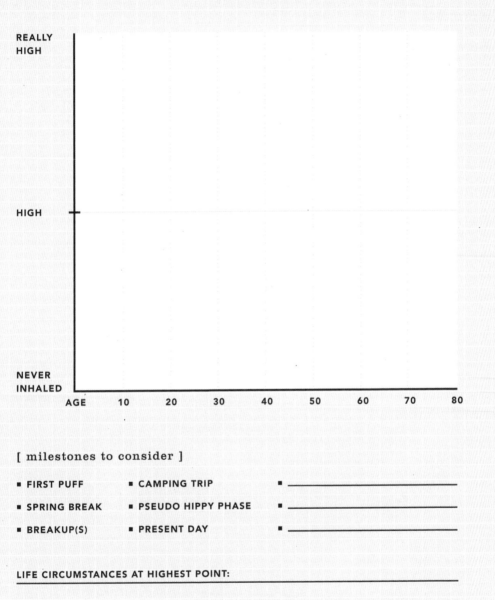

REALLY
HIGH

HIGH ┼

NEVER
INHALED

AGE   10   20   30   40   50   60   70   80

[milestones to consider]

■ FIRST PUFF   ■ CAMPING TRIP   ■ _____

■ SPRING BREAK   ■ PSEUDO HIPPY PHASE   ■ _____

■ BREAKUP(S)   ■ PRESENT DAY   ■ _____

LIFE CIRCUMSTANCES AT HIGHEST POINT: _____

_____

_____

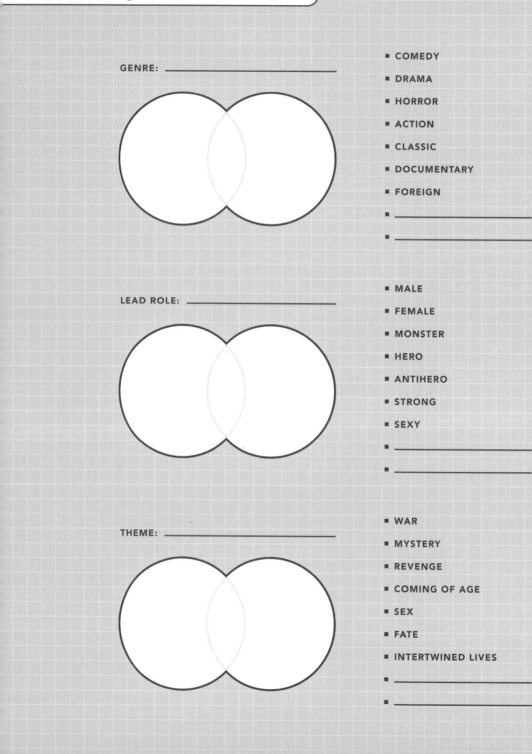

GENRE: _____

- COMEDY
- DRAMA
- HORROR
- ACTION
- CLASSIC
- DOCUMENTARY
- FOREIGN
- _____
- _____

LEAD ROLE: _____

- MALE
- FEMALE
- MONSTER
- HERO
- ANTIHERO
- STRONG
- SEXY
- _____
- _____

THEME: _____

- WAR
- MYSTERY
- REVENGE
- COMING OF AGE
- SEX
- FATE
- INTERTWINED LIVES
- _____
- _____

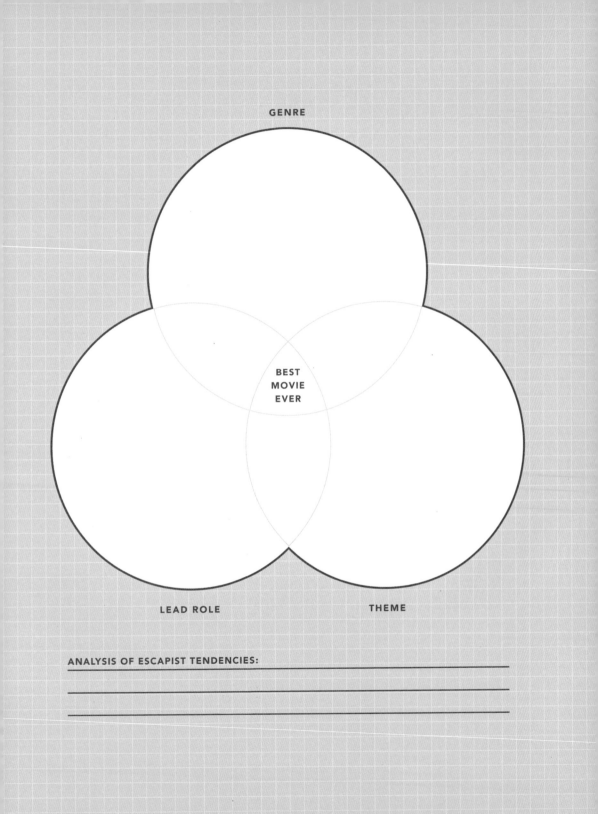

GENRE

BEST
MOVIE
EVER

LEAD ROLE

THEME

ANALYSIS OF ESCAPIST TENDENCIES:

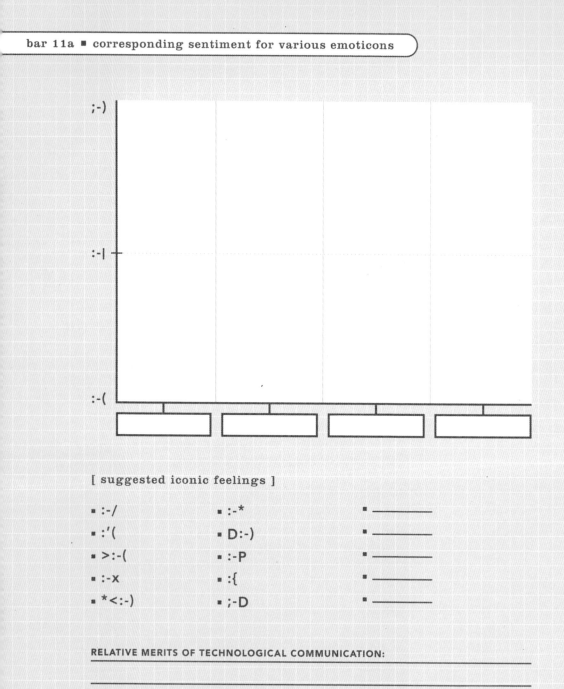

;-)

:-|

:-(

[suggested iconic feelings]

- :-/
- :'(
- >:-(
- :-x
- *<:-)

- :-*
- D:-)
- :-P
- :{
- ;-D

- _____
- _____
- _____
- _____
- _____

RELATIVE MERITS OF TECHNOLOGICAL COMMUNICATION:

_____

_____

RELATIVE DRAWBACKS OF TECHNOLOGICAL COMMUNICATION:

_____

_____

GOLD

SILVER

BRONZE

[suggested indicators of your place on the totem pole]

- INTRAMURAL SPORTS
- POSITION IN GRADUATING CLASS
- TROPHIES ON MANTEL
- NUMBER OF CARS
- SALARY
- MONEY LOST ON BETS

- _____
- _____
- _____
- _____
- _____
- _____

supplement 12b ■ mathematical breakdown of the importance of winning

[>, <, (or) =]

- VICTORY _____ FRIENDSHIP
- VICTORY _____ POPULARITY
- VICTORY _____ STABILITY

- VICTORY _____ CONSENSUS
- VICTORY _____ HAPPINESS
- VICTORY _____ SURVIVAL

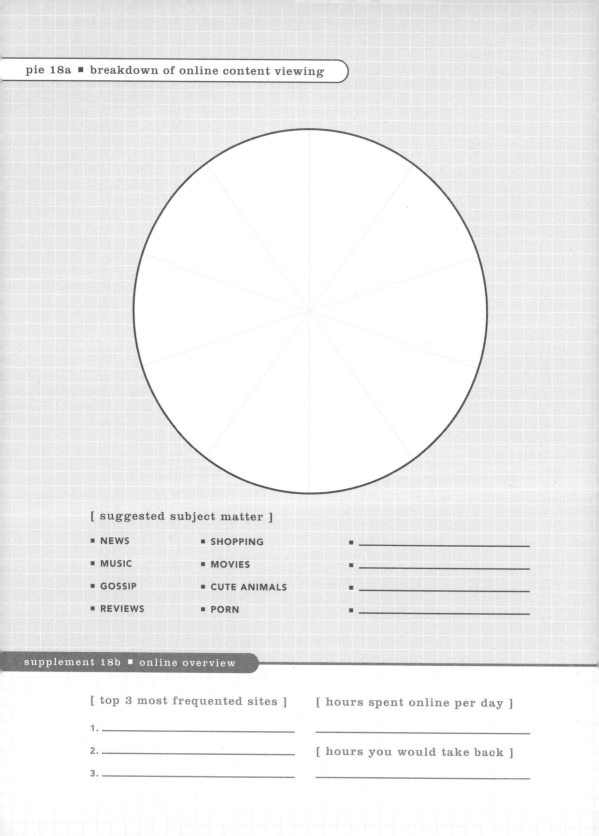

[suggested subject matter]

- NEWS
- MUSIC
- GOSSIP
- REVIEWS

- SHOPPING
- MOVIES
- CUTE ANIMALS
- PORN

- _____
- _____
- _____
- _____

supplement 18b ■ online overview

[top 3 most frequented sites]

1. _____

2. _____

3. _____

[hours spent online per day]

_____

[hours you would take back]

_____

RELATIONSHIP #1: _____

LOVE	HATE

RELATIONSHIP #2: _____

LOVE	HATE

RELATIONSHIP #3: _____

LOVE	HATE

RELATIONSHIP #4: _____

LOVE	HATE

RELATIONSHIP #5: _____

LOVE	HATE

[suggested relationships]

- PARENTS
- SIBLINGS
- PARTNER

- COWORKER
- BEST FRIEND
- FOOD

- _____
- _____
- _____

☐ CRITICISM

☐ NEEDINESS

☐ BAD HYGIENE

☐ COMPETITIVENESS

☐ NARCISSISM

☐ IMMATURITY

☐ DISLOYALTY

☐ POOR STORYTELLING

☐ OBSTINACY

☐ HIGH-PITCHED VOICE

☐ STUPIDITY

☐ NATURAL THINNESS

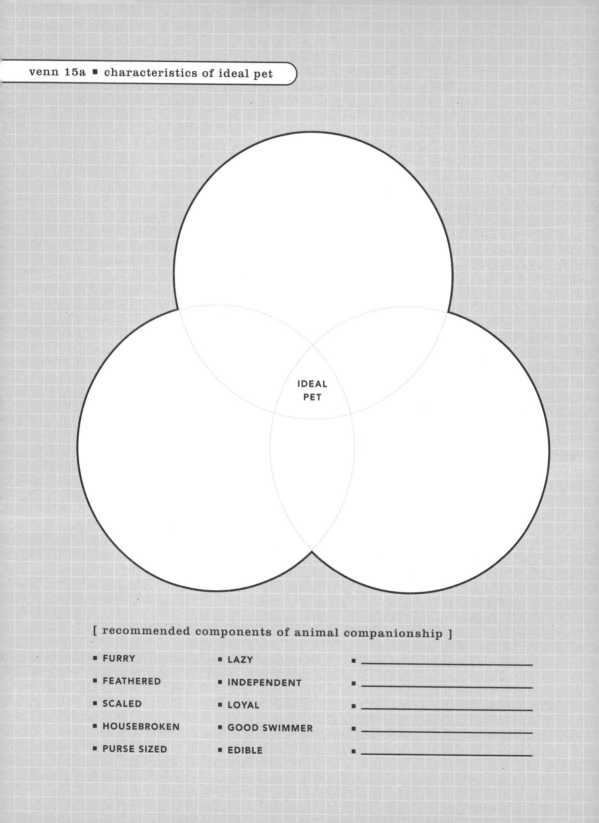

IDEAL
PET

[recommended components of animal companionship]

- FURRY
- FEATHERED
- SCALED
- HOUSEBROKEN
- PURSE SIZED

- LAZY
- INDEPENDENT
- LOYAL
- GOOD SWIMMER
- EDIBLE

- _____
- _____
- _____
- _____
- _____

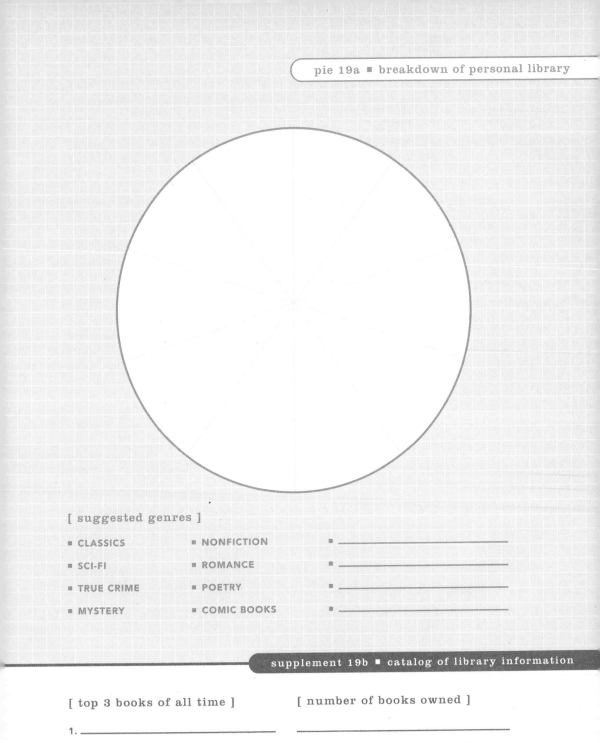

[suggested genres]

■ CLASSICS   ■ NONFICTION   ■ _____

■ SCI-FI   ■ ROMANCE   ■ _____

■ TRUE CRIME   ■ POETRY   ■ _____

■ MYSTERY   ■ COMIC BOOKS   ■ _____

[top 3 books of all time]   [number of books owned]

1. _____   _____

2. _____   [percentage of books read]

3. _____   _____

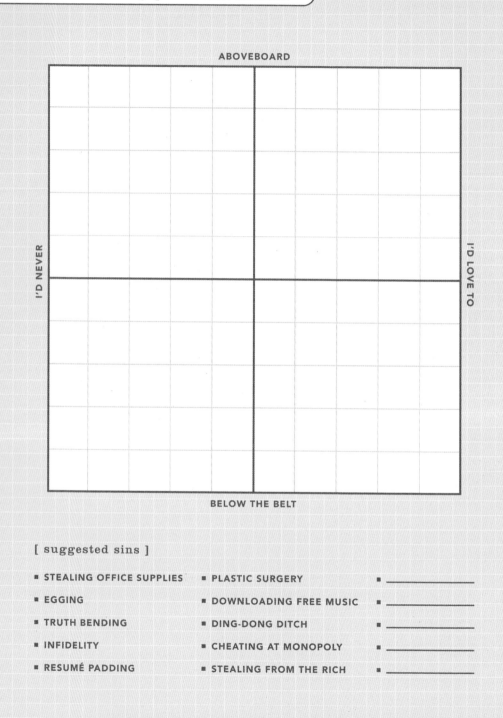

ABOVEBOARD

I'D NEVER

I'D LOVE TO

BELOW THE BELT

[suggested sins]

- STEALING OFFICE SUPPLIES
- EGGING
- TRUTH BENDING
- INFIDELITY
- RESUMÉ PADDING

- PLASTIC SURGERY
- DOWNLOADING FREE MUSIC
- DING-DONG DITCH
- CHEATING AT MONOPOLY
- STEALING FROM THE RICH

- _____
- _____
- _____
- _____
- _____

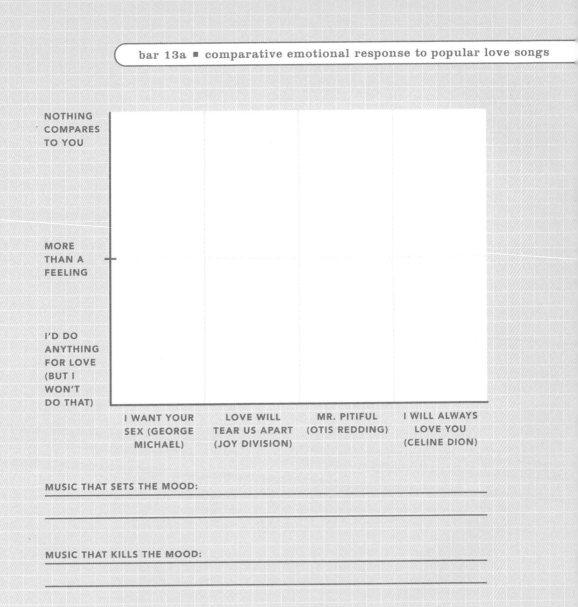

NOTHING COMPARES TO YOU

MORE THAN A FEELING

I'D DO ANYTHING FOR LOVE (BUT I WON'T DO THAT)

I WANT YOUR SEX (GEORGE MICHAEL)

LOVE WILL TEAR US APART (JOY DIVISION)

MR. PITIFUL (OTIS REDDING)

I WILL ALWAYS LOVE YOU (CELINE DION)

MUSIC THAT SETS THE MOOD: _____

_____

MUSIC THAT KILLS THE MOOD: _____

_____

supplement 13b ■ mathematical breakdown of the importance of love

[>, <, (or) =]

- LOVE _____ FOOD
- LOVE _____ TELEVISION
- LOVE _____ MONEY

- LOVE _____ SEX
- LOVE _____ REVENGE
- LOVE _____ FLAT STOMACH

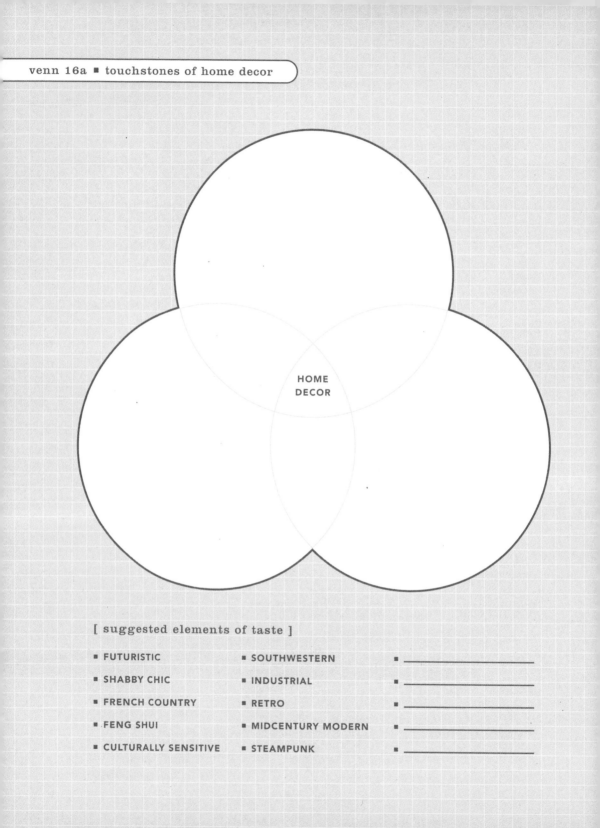

HOME
DECOR

[suggested elements of taste]

- FUTURISTIC
- SHABBY CHIC
- FRENCH COUNTRY
- FENG SHUI
- CULTURALLY SENSITIVE

- SOUTHWESTERN
- INDUSTRIAL
- RETRO
- MIDCENTURY MODERN
- STEAMPUNK

- _____
- _____
- _____
- _____
- _____

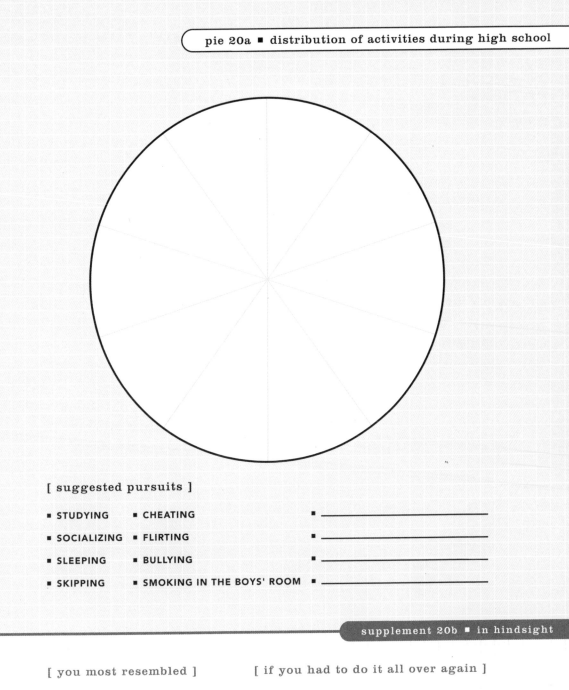

[suggested pursuits]

- STUDYING   - CHEATING
- SOCIALIZING - FLIRTING
- SLEEPING   - BULLYING
- SKIPPING   - SMOKING IN THE BOYS' ROOM

■ _____
■ _____
■ _____
■ _____

supplement 20b ■ in hindsight

[you most resembled]

□ JOCK   □ REBEL
□ CHEERLEADER □ CLASS CLOWN
□ NERD   □ INVISIBLE

[if you had to do it all over again]

_____
_____
_____

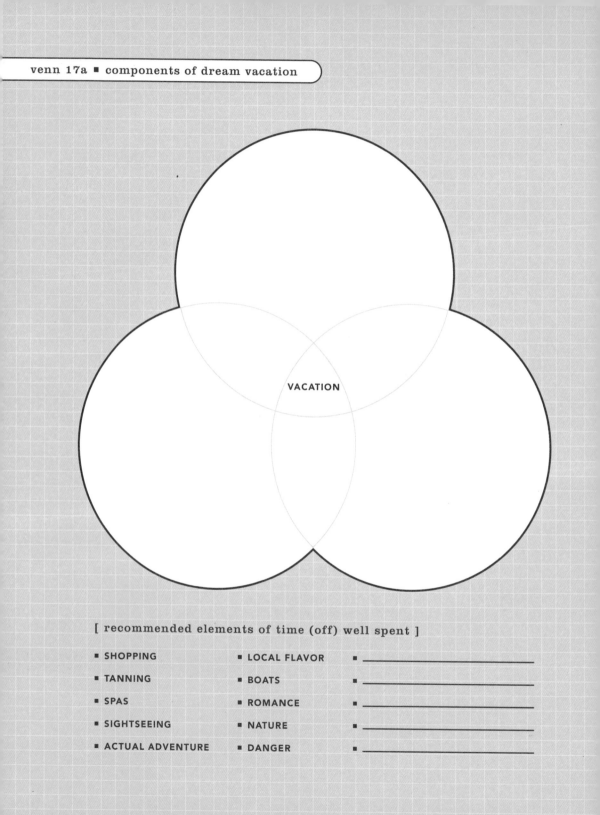

VACATION

[recommended elements of time (off) well spent]

- SHOPPING
- TANNING
- SPAS
- SIGHTSEEING
- ACTUAL ADVENTURE

- LOCAL FLAVOR
- BOATS
- ROMANCE
- NATURE
- DANGER

- _____
- _____
- _____
- _____
- _____

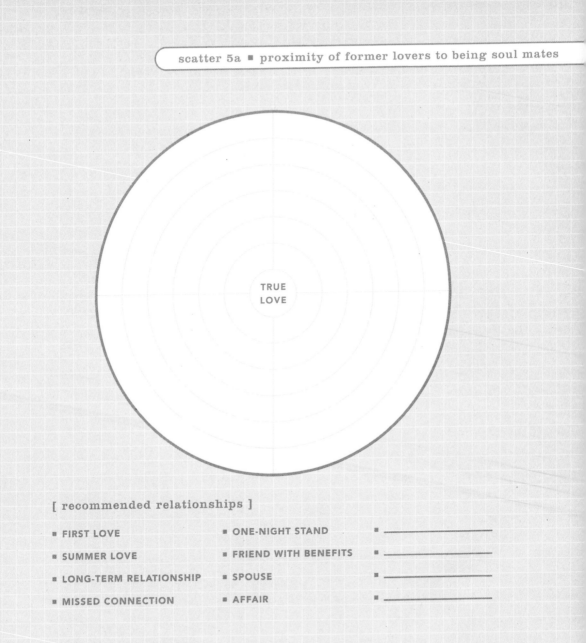

TRUE
LOVE

[recommended relationships]

■ FIRST LOVE   ■ ONE-NIGHT STAND   ■ _____

■ SUMMER LOVE   ■ FRIEND WITH BENEFITS   ■ _____

■ LONG-TERM RELATIONSHIP   ■ SPOUSE   ■ _____

■ MISSED CONNECTION   ■ AFFAIR   ■ _____

DO SOUL MATES EVEN EXIST?: _____

_____

_____

_____

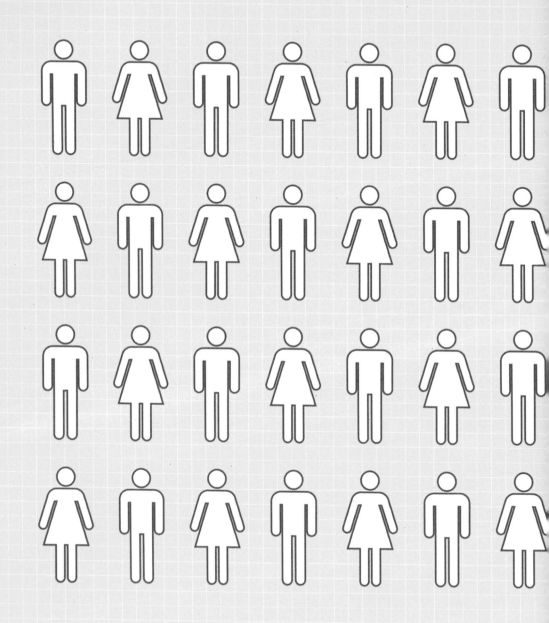

instructions:
[fill in a body to represent each lover]

CONCLUSIONS BASED ON GRAPHIC EVIDENCE: _____

_____

_____

pie 21a ■ breakdown of good deeds

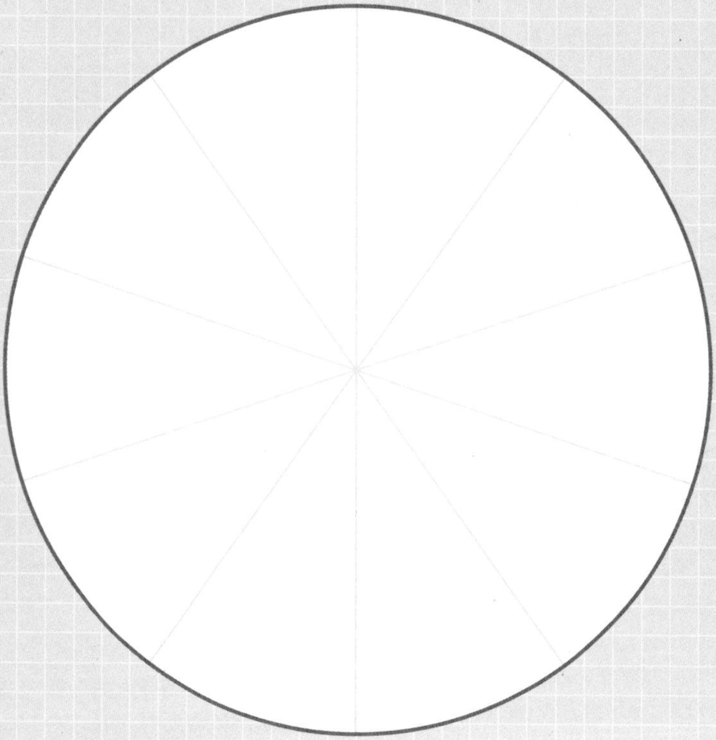

[possible public services]

- VOLUNTEERING
- RECYCLING
- GIVING BENEFIT OF THE DOUBT
- CONTROLLING TEMPER
- DONATING MONEY
- ASSISTING ELDERS
- HANDING OUT COMPLIMENTS
- MAKING BED
- SAYING THANK YOU
- SMOKING OUTSIDE

- ______________________
- ______________________
- ______________________
- ______________________
- ______________________
- ______________________
- ______________________
- ______________________
- ______________________
- ______________________

16TH BIRTHDAY: _____

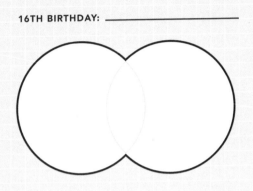

21ST BIRTHDAY: _____

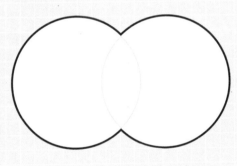

[suggested elements of landmark years past]

- CAKE
- SURPRISES
- AGE JOKES
- PRESENTS
- PIÑATA
- MALT LIQUOR
- DEBAUCHERY
- DREAD
- RESIGNATION
- DISAPPOINTMENT
- _____
- _____
- _____
- _____
- _____

LAST BIRTHDAY: _____

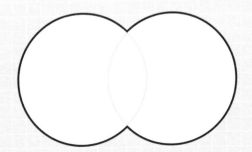

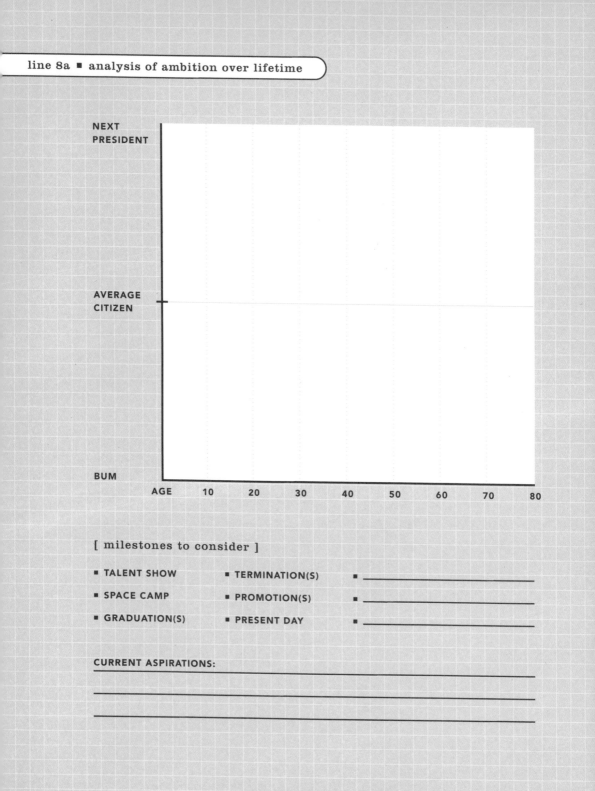

NEXT
PRESIDENT

AVERAGE
CITIZEN

BUM

AGE   10   20   30   40   50   60   70   80

[milestones to consider]

■ TALENT SHOW   ■ TERMINATION(S)   ■ _____

■ SPACE CAMP   ■ PROMOTION(S)   ■ _____

■ GRADUATION(S)   ■ PRESENT DAY   ■ _____

CURRENT ASPIRATIONS: _____

_____

_____

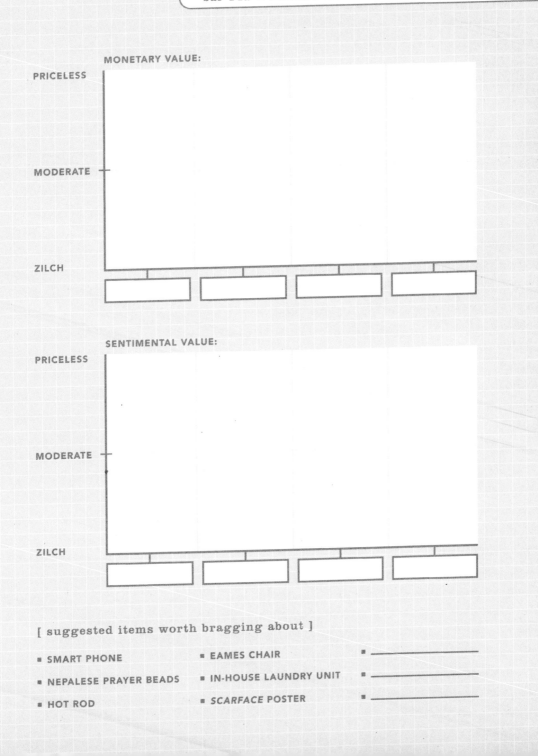

MONETARY VALUE:

PRICELESS

MODERATE

ZILCH

SENTIMENTAL VALUE:

PRICELESS

MODERATE

ZILCH

[suggested items worth bragging about]

- SMART PHONE
- NEPALESE PRAYER BEADS
- HOT ROD

- EAMES CHAIR
- IN-HOUSE LAUNDRY UNIT
- *SCARFACE* POSTER

- _____
- _____
- _____

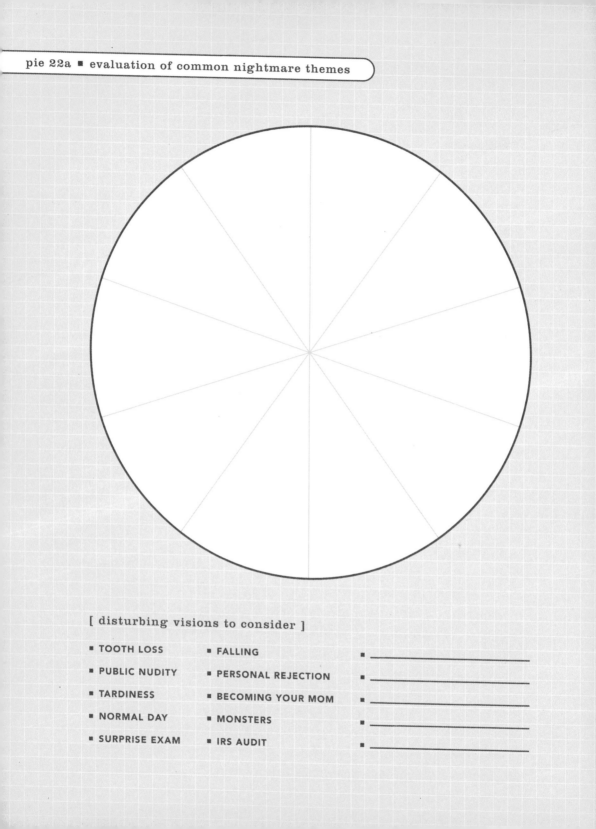

pie 22a ▪ evaluation of common nightmare themes

[disturbing visions to consider]

- TOOTH LOSS   ▪ FALLING
- PUBLIC NUDITY   ▪ PERSONAL REJECTION
- TARDINESS   ▪ BECOMING YOUR MOM
- NORMAL DAY   ▪ MONSTERS
- SURPRISE EXAM   ▪ IRS AUDIT

▪ _____
▪ _____
▪ _____
▪ _____
▪ _____

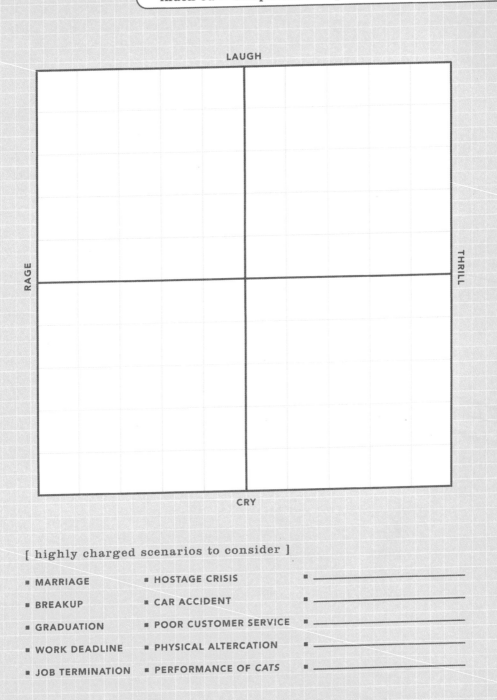

LAUGH

RAGE

THRILL

CRY

[highly charged scenarios to consider]

- MARRIAGE
- BREAKUP
- GRADUATION
- WORK DEADLINE
- JOB TERMINATION

- HOSTAGE CRISIS
- CAR ACCIDENT
- POOR CUSTOMER SERVICE
- PHYSICAL ALTERCATION
- PERFORMANCE OF *CATS*

- _____
- _____
- _____
- _____
- _____

EX #1: _____

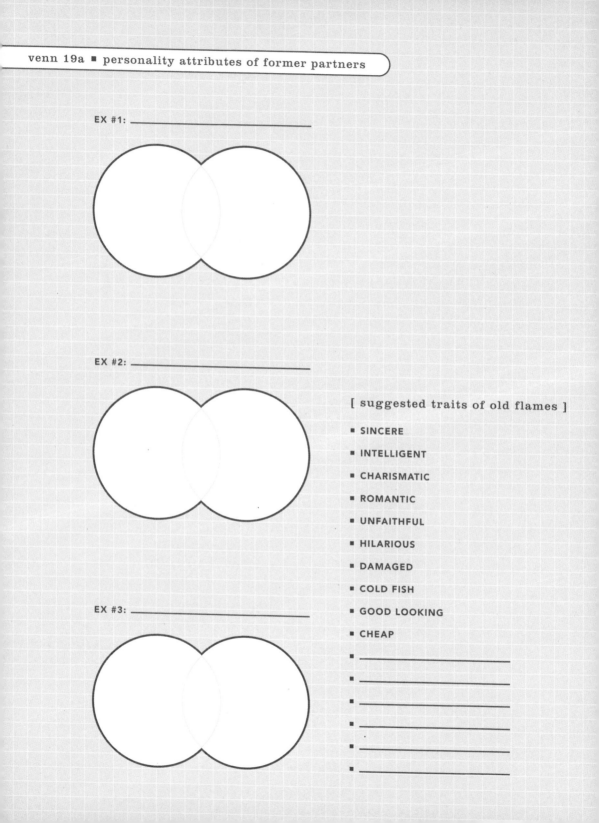

EX #2: _____

[suggested traits of old flames]

▪ SINCERE

▪ INTELLIGENT

▪ CHARISMATIC

▪ ROMANTIC

▪ UNFAITHFUL

▪ HILARIOUS

▪ DAMAGED

▪ COLD FISH

EX #3: _____

▪ GOOD LOOKING

▪ CHEAP

▪ _____

▪ _____

▪ _____

▪ _____

▪ _____

▪ _____

CONFIDANT #1: _____

LIE	TRUTH

CONFIDANT #2: _____

LIE	TRUTH

CONFIDANT #3: _____

LIE	TRUTH

CONFIDANT #4: _____

LIE	TRUTH

CONFIDANT #5: _____

LIE	TRUTH

[suggested connections]

- PARENTS
- SIBLINGS
- BOSS

- PARTNER
- BEST FRIEND
- IRS

- _____
- _____
- _____

supplement 6b ▪ situations wherein lying is justified

☐ JOB INTERVIEWS   ☐ DRESSING ROOMS   ☐ ONLINE

☐ HOSPITALS   ☐ REGARDING MEALS   ☐ COLLEGE CLASSROOMS

☐ LITERARY SALONS   ☐ BREAKUPS   ☐ BOSS'S OFFICE

☐ ART SHOWS   ☐ CONVERSATIONS WITH KIDS ☐ TO AVOID JAIL TIME

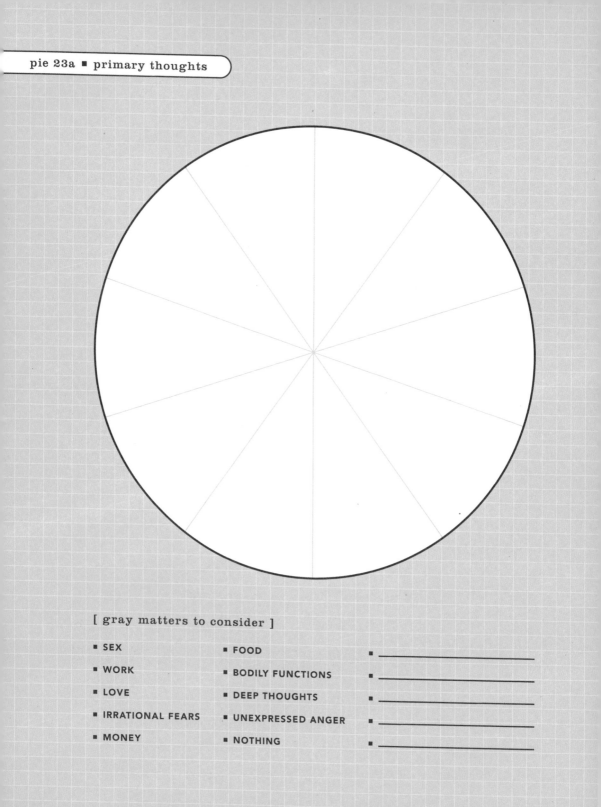

pie 23a ▪ primary thoughts

[gray matters to consider]

- SEX
- WORK
- LOVE
- IRRATIONAL FEARS
- MONEY

- FOOD
- BODILY FUNCTIONS
- DEEP THOUGHTS
- UNEXPRESSED ANGER
- NOTHING

- _____
- _____
- _____
- _____
- _____

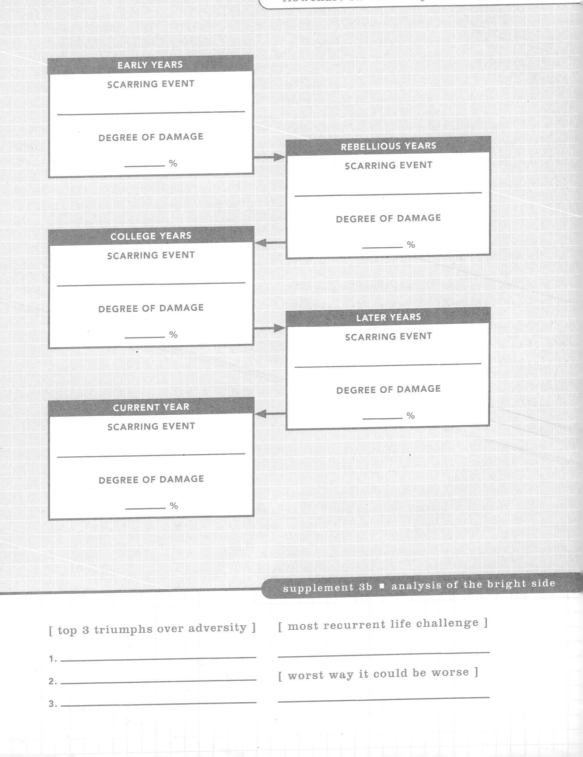

EARLY YEARS

SCARRING EVENT

_____

DEGREE OF DAMAGE

_____ %

REBELLIOUS YEARS

SCARRING EVENT

_____

DEGREE OF DAMAGE

_____ %

COLLEGE YEARS

SCARRING EVENT

_____

DEGREE OF DAMAGE

_____ %

LATER YEARS

SCARRING EVENT

_____

DEGREE OF DAMAGE

_____ %

CURRENT YEAR

SCARRING EVENT

_____

DEGREE OF DAMAGE

_____ %

supplement 3b ∎ analysis of the bright side

[top 3 triumphs over adversity]

1. _____

2. _____

3. _____

[most recurrent life challenge]

_____

[worst way it could be worse]

_____

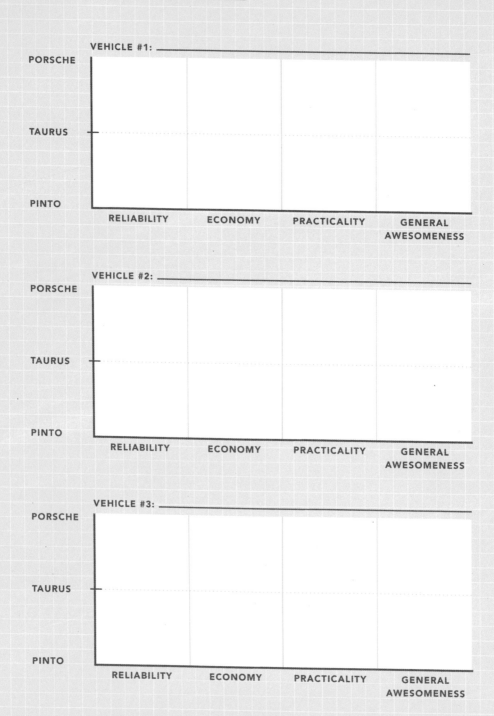

VEHICLE #1: _____

PORSCHE

TAURUS

PINTO

RELIABILITY   ECONOMY   PRACTICALITY   GENERAL AWESOMENESS

VEHICLE #2: _____

PORSCHE

TAURUS

PINTO

RELIABILITY   ECONOMY   PRACTICALITY   GENERAL AWESOMENESS

VEHICLE #3: _____

PORSCHE

TAURUS

PINTO

RELIABILITY   ECONOMY   PRACTICALITY   GENERAL AWESOMENESS

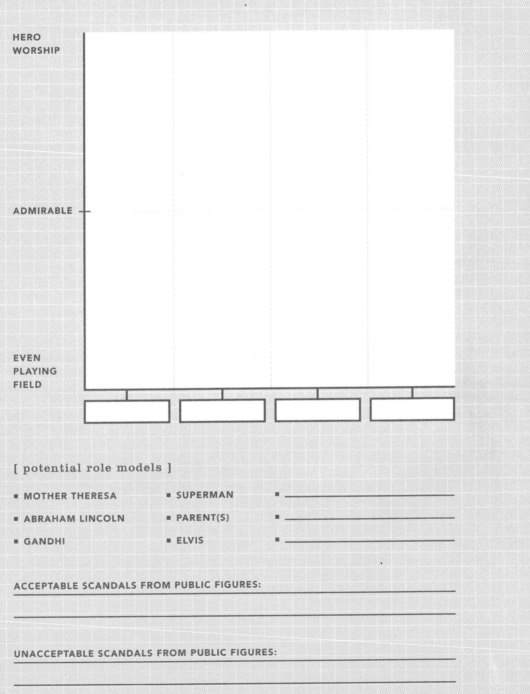

HERO
WORSHIP

ADMIRABLE —

EVEN
PLAYING
FIELD

[potential role models]

▪ MOTHER THERESA   ▪ SUPERMAN   ▪ _____

▪ ABRAHAM LINCOLN   ▪ PARENT(S)   ▪ _____

▪ GANDHI   ▪ ELVIS   ▪ _____

ACCEPTABLE SCANDALS FROM PUBLIC FIGURES: _____
_____
_____

UNACCEPTABLE SCANDALS FROM PUBLIC FIGURES: _____
_____
_____

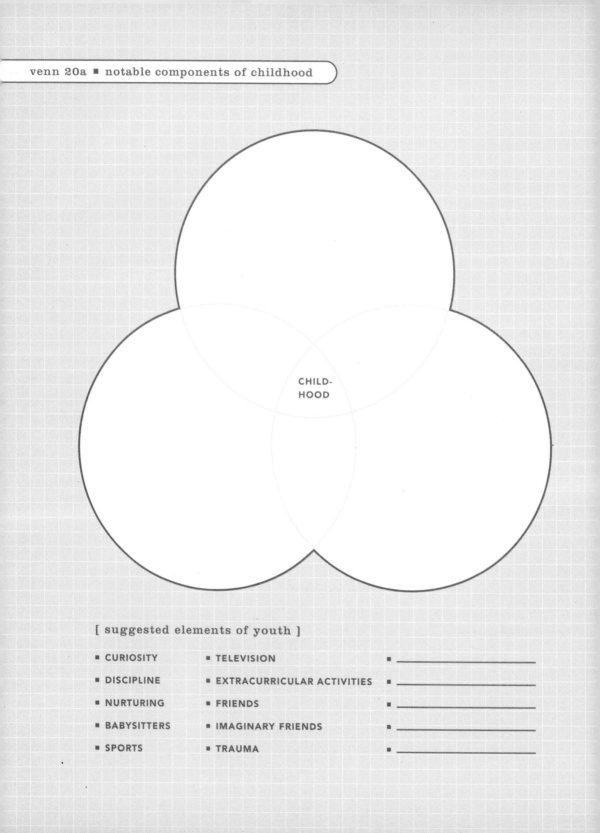

CHILD-
HOOD

[suggested elements of youth]

- CURIOSITY   ■ TELEVISION   ■ _____
- DISCIPLINE   ■ EXTRACURRICULAR ACTIVITIES   ■ _____
- NURTURING   ■ FRIENDS   ■ _____
- BABYSITTERS   ■ IMAGINARY FRIENDS   ■ _____
- SPORTS   ■ TRAUMA   ■ _____

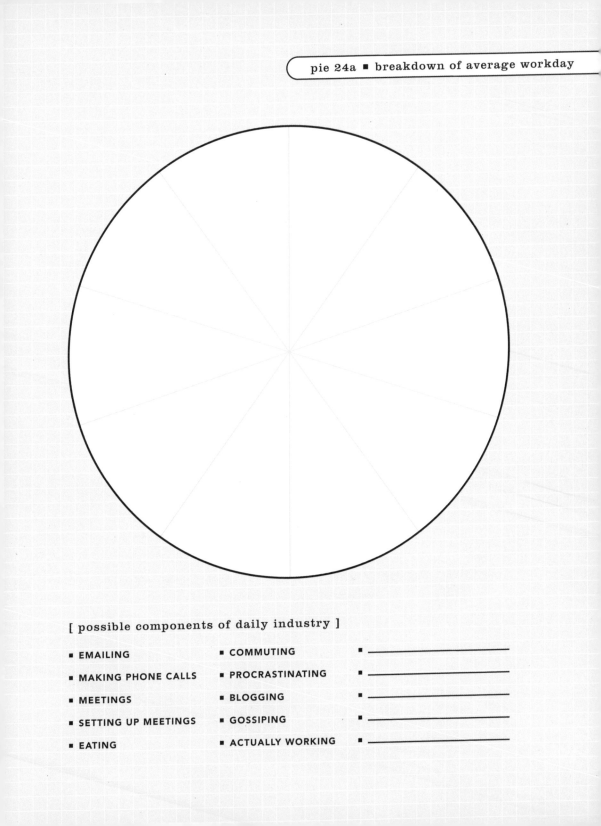

[possible components of daily industry]

- EMAILING
- MAKING PHONE CALLS
- MEETINGS
- SETTING UP MEETINGS
- EATING

- COMMUTING
- PROCRASTINATING
- BLOGGING
- GOSSIPING
- ACTUALLY WORKING

- _____
- _____
- _____
- _____
- _____

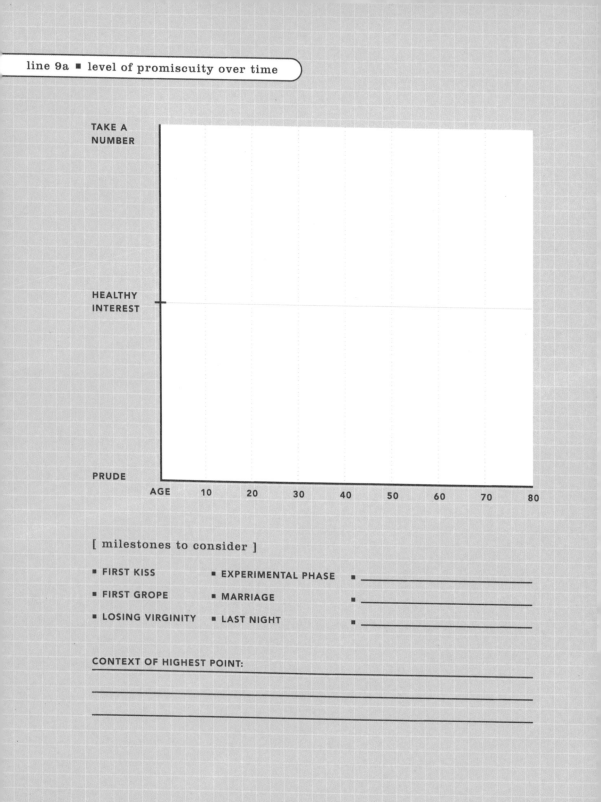

TAKE A
NUMBER

HEALTHY
INTEREST

PRUDE

AGE   10   20   30   40   50   60   70   80

[milestones to consider]

▪ FIRST KISS   ▪ EXPERIMENTAL PHASE   ▪ _____

▪ FIRST GROPE   ▪ MARRIAGE   ▪ _____

▪ LOSING VIRGINITY   ▪ LAST NIGHT   ▪ _____

CONTEXT OF HIGHEST POINT: _____

_____

_____

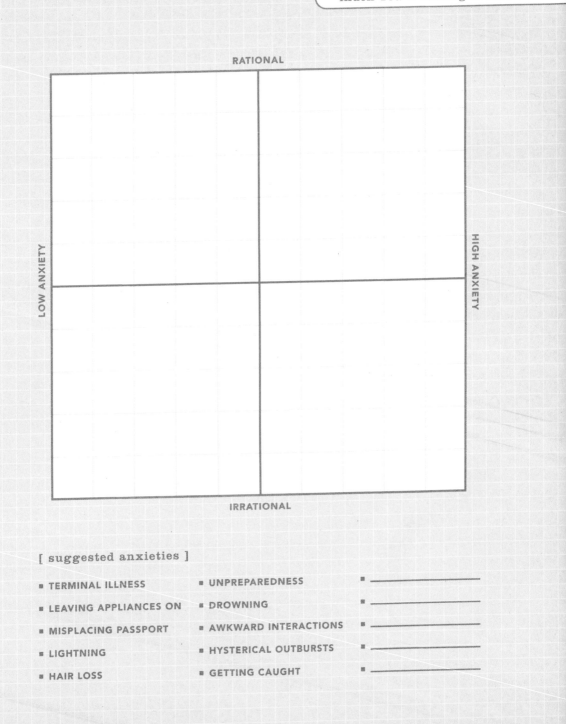

RATIONAL

LOW ANXIETY

HIGH ANXIETY

IRRATIONAL

[suggested anxieties]

- TERMINAL ILLNESS
- LEAVING APPLIANCES ON
- MISPLACING PASSPORT
- LIGHTNING
- HAIR LOSS

- UNPREPAREDNESS
- DROWNING
- AWKWARD INTERACTIONS
- HYSTERICAL OUTBURSTS
- GETTING CAUGHT

- _____
- _____
- _____
- _____
- _____

EX-BOSS #1: _____

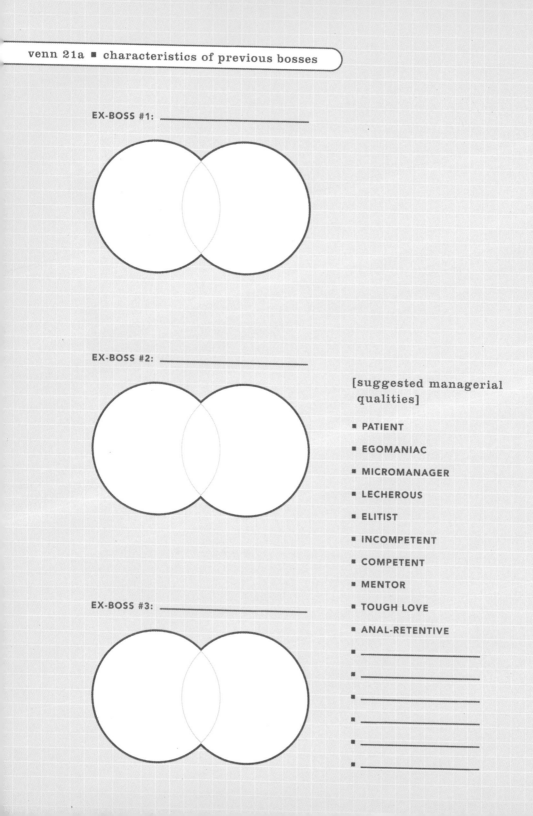

EX-BOSS #2: _____

[suggested managerial qualities]

- PATIENT
- EGOMANIAC
- MICROMANAGER
- LECHEROUS
- ELITIST
- INCOMPETENT
- COMPETENT
- MENTOR
- TOUGH LOVE
- ANAL-RETENTIVE
- _____
- _____
- _____
- _____
- _____
- _____

EX-BOSS #3: _____

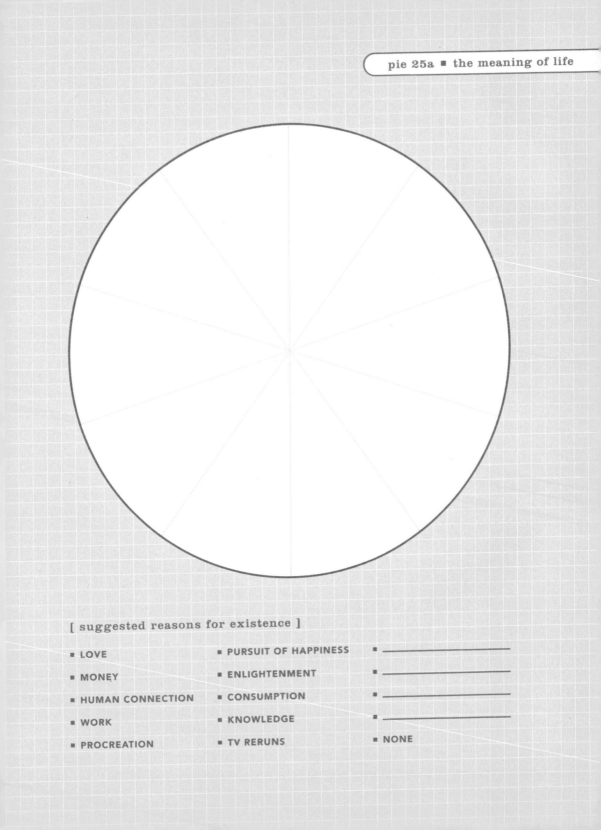

[suggested reasons for existence]

- LOVE
- MONEY
- HUMAN CONNECTION
- WORK
- PROCREATION

- PURSUIT OF HAPPINESS
- ENLIGHTENMENT
- CONSUMPTION
- KNOWLEDGE
- TV RERUNS

- _____
- _____
- _____
- _____
- NONE

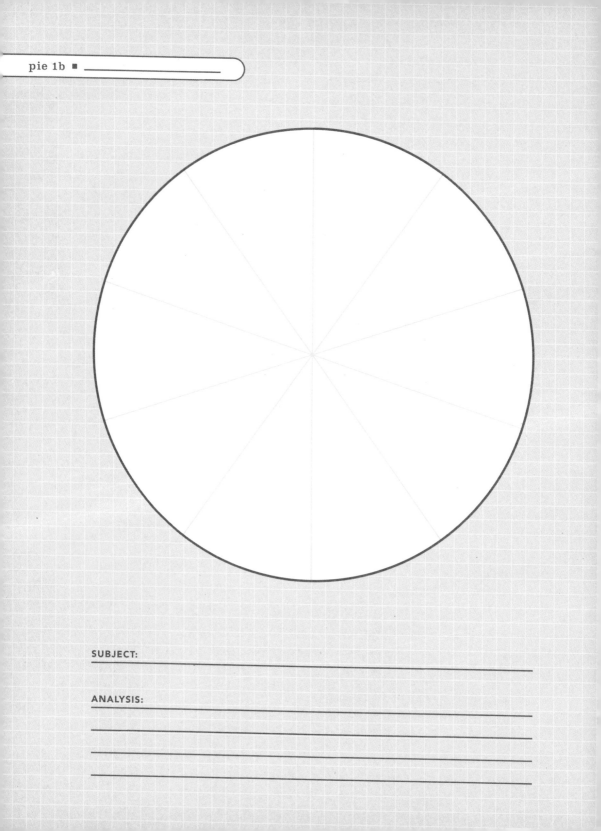

SUBJECT: _____

ANALYSIS: _____

_____

_____

_____

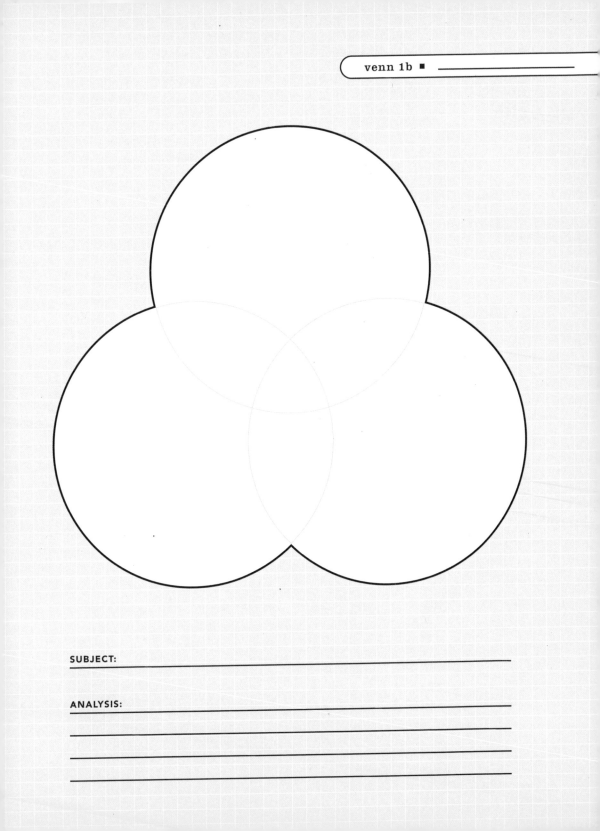

SUBJECT: _____

ANALYSIS: _____

_____

_____

_____

_____

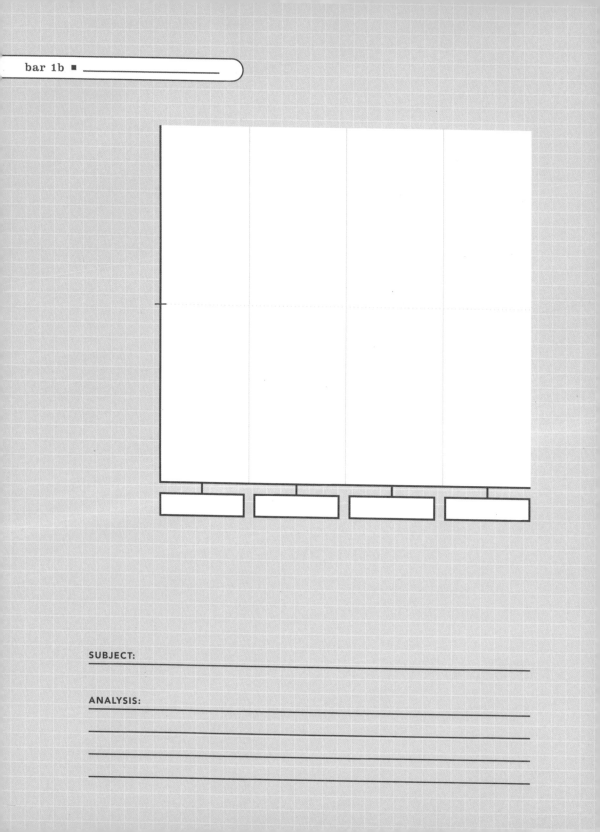

SUBJECT: _____

ANALYSIS: _____

_____

_____

_____

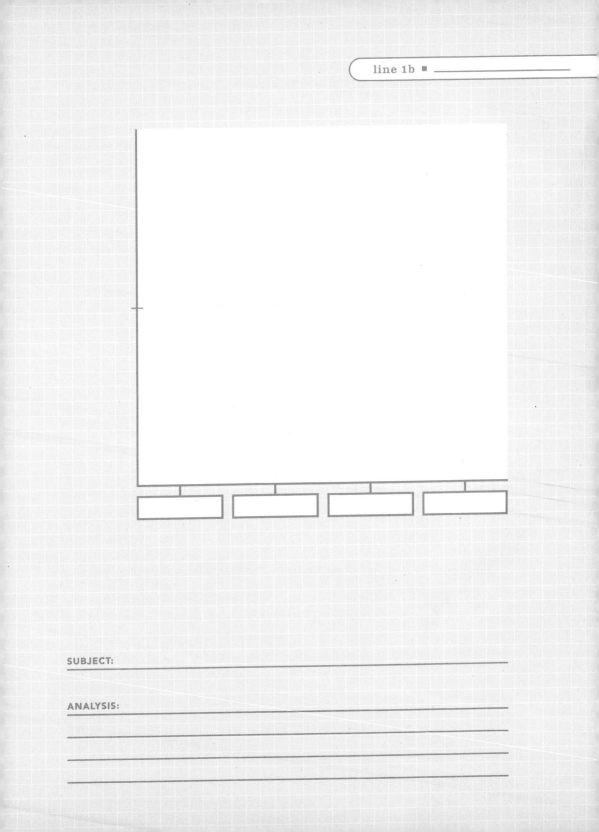

SUBJECT: _____

ANALYSIS: _____
_____
_____
_____

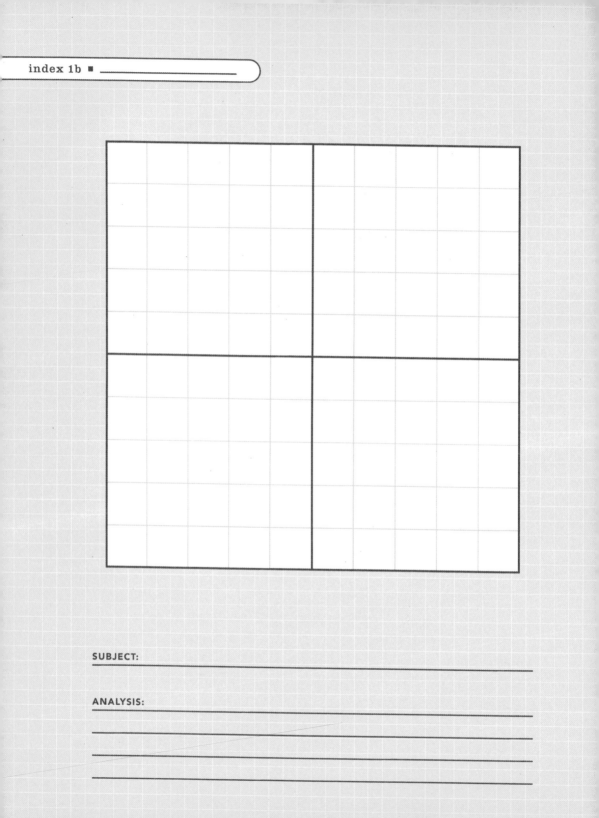

SUBJECT:

ANALYSIS:

#1: _____

#2: _____

#3: _____

#4: _____

#5: _____

SUBJECT: _____

ANALYSIS: _____
_____
_____
_____

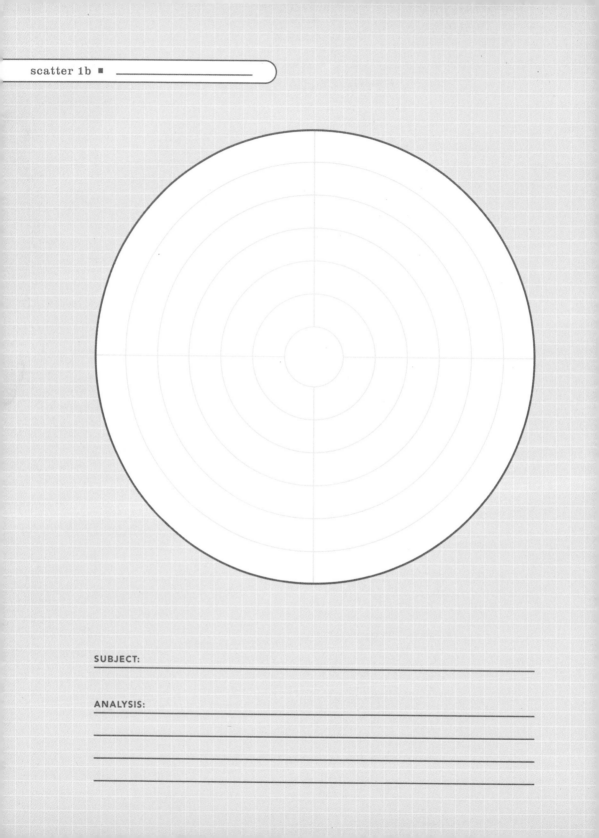

SUBJECT: _____

ANALYSIS: _____

_____

_____

_____

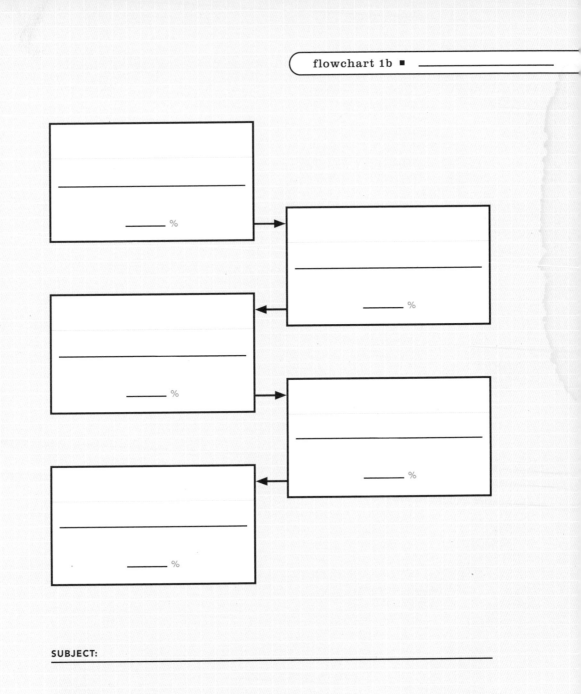

SUBJECT: _____

ANALYSIS: _____
_____
_____
_____